Learning to Read with
Clues to **Meaning**

Ann L. Staman

E

Educators Publishing Service, Inc.
Cambridge and Toronto

To the Teacher

Clues to Meaning is a beginning reading series that treats phonetic decoding as one strategy among many for unlocking meaning from a text. The books encourage readers to use semantic and syntactic clues, as well as sounds, to decipher unknown words. Sound-letter correspondences and phonetic patterns are designed to invite children to notice the phonemic similarities and differences between words.

After becoming familiar with a phonetic pattern, students are encouraged to use phonetic strategies in conjunction with pictorial, semantic, and contextual clues as they work with a variety of realistic reading situations. Beginning readers learn to use phonics the way experienced readers do—in a flexible and strategic manner—as they engage in meaningful reading and writing activities.

In This Book

Cover design and text illustration by Anne Lord

Dedicated to Mary Baltren, who teaches first grade
in Belchertown, Massachusetts.

Thanks to Dorothy Miller
for all her patience, encouragement, and editorial assistance.

May 2002 Printing

Short vowels are sound clues. Here are the short vowel sounds.

ă
alligator

ĕ
elephant

ĭ
iguana

ŏ
octopus

ŭ
umbrella bird

● Write vowels:

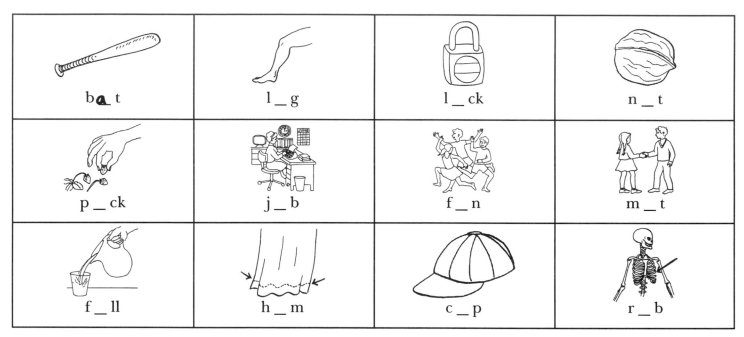

b**a**t	l _ g	l _ ck	n _ t
p _ ck	j _ b	f _ n	m _ t
f _ ll	h _ m	c _ p	r _ b

● Circle:

bed / bad / bid / Deb	Cass / skin / kiss / kits	pad / ped / dip / pod	dug / dog / gab / bug
lee / well / lay / yell	tick / tock / tuck / tack	fun / fix / cuff / cud	sax / six / socks / sass
wit / ten / wed / wet	sob / rocks / ducks / box	hip / pen / hop / hap	boss / buzz / bass / sub

2

● Where do the words in the box belong?

(fox)	mud	pot
if	mop	rock
cab	mad	hill
bed	den	had
T.V. set	dam	rug

INSIDE	OUTSIDE
1. _____	1. _fox_____
2. _____	2. _____
3. _____	3. _____
4. _____	4. _____
5. _____	5. _____
6. _____	6. _____

● Fill in the blanks with the words from the box.

POTS   its   Eggs   Hub   Pets   Fix

Dog   Gum   Dots   Had   Pens   Sets

Ham
and
_____
$3.50

POTS_____ **AND PANS $10**

T.V.
_____
**$10.00
off**

*Red
Felt-tip*

_____

_____
– dogs
– cats
– lizards

*99¢
pack
of
10*

Hot _____
*in a bun
$1.75*

_____ *caps*
(all sizes)

**Mr. San
the
_____-It
Man**

Dot-to-_____

4

Here is a **trick** for reading some longer words. Look for **small words** within big **compound words.**

hilltop = hill + top
       w   w
	backpack = back + pack
	         w w

● Put **w** and **w** under the 2 **small words** in each **compound word**. Then draw a line between the 2 small words. Read them.

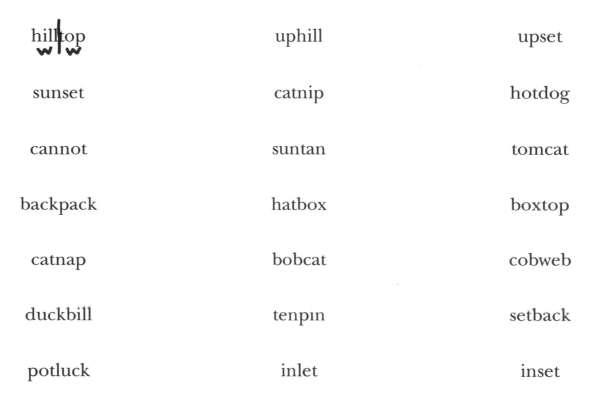

hill|top w w	uphill	upset
sunset	catnip	hotdog
cannot	suntan	tomcat
backpack	hatbox	boxtop
catnap	bobcat	cobweb
duckbill	tenpin	setback
potluck	inlet	inset

5

● Read the meaning and number of letters. Then find the word with that meaning and number of letters in the big word on the right. Put a line under it.

Meaning	Number of Letters	Hidden Words
Dog or Cat	3	PUP<u>PET</u>
Glove for catching a ball	4	MITTEN
We; you and I	2	RUSTY
Part of the body	3	CRIBS
To jump on one foot	3	SHOPPING
Sick; not well	3	PILLOW
Total; what you add up	3	POSSUM
Not out; inside	2	TWINS
Number 10	3	BITTEN
Opposite of more	4	BLESS
Tin container	3	CANDLE
To be; I ____	2	DAMP
Big car	3	DIVAN
Strong animal, like a steer	2	BOXER

A **compound word** is a big word made of two smaller words.

cob   web

● Draw a line to make a **compound word.**

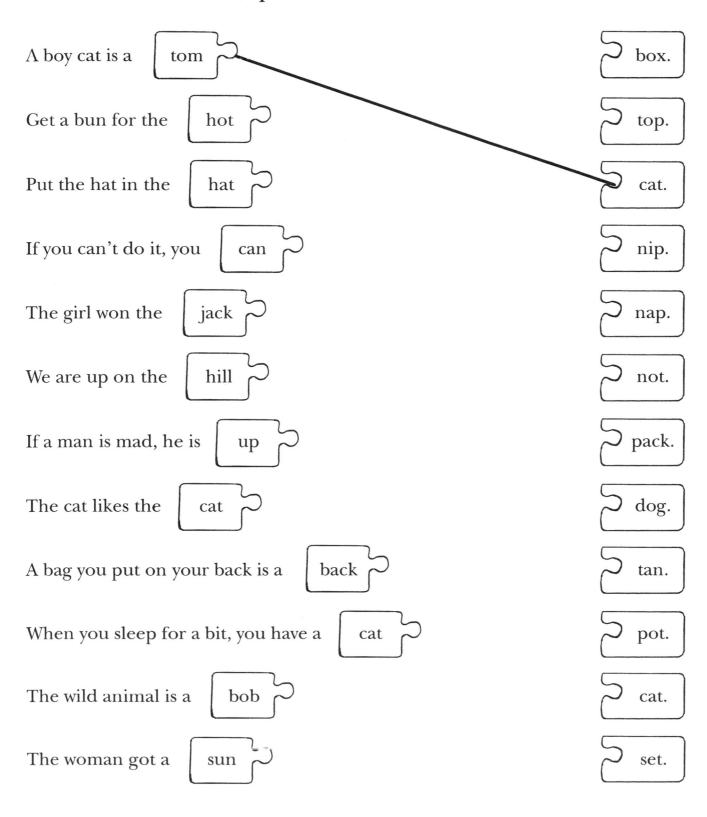

A boy cat is a [tom] ——————————— [box.]

Get a bun for the [hot] [top.]

Put the hat in the [hat] [cat.]

If you can't do it, you [can] [nip.]

The girl won the [jack] [nap.]

We are up on the [hill] [not.]

If a man is mad, he is [up] [pack.]

The cat likes the [cat] [dog.]

A bag you put on your back is a [back] [tan.]

When you sleep for a bit, you have a [cat] [pot.]

The wild animal is a [bob] [cat.]

The woman got a [sun] [set.]

All the letters that are not vowels are **consonants**. Sometimes 2 or 3 consonants stick together in a word. Then we call them **consonant blends**.

sp + ot = **sp**ot   **Fr** + ed = **Fr**ed

dr + ag = **dr**ag   **cl** + uck = **cl**uck

● Circle the word:

brick block bring drink trick	dens bled sped sled sent	stops stamp spent sets steps	lags brag flag flop flog
glass grass class brass grabs	shim shrimp swan swim spin	from frog flog golf gruff	tricks trucks tracks scratch stacks
quack quit crack clack cluck	bram rump mend dream drum	crick clack quack crack crank	bricks blacks blocks blots slobs
scratch splint squash crash splash	spring string sprig strip strap	clack cluck clock chock clonk	grab grad drab grub brag

8

● Cross out the word on each pad that does not belong:

Pad 1:
Frasco
~~stuck~~
Wanda
Lan Deng
Scott

Pad 2:
milk
snack
plum
clams
swing

Pad 3:
kept
skunk
lamb
elk
frog

Pad 4:
nest
pond
sand
quick
stump

Pad 5:
hand
fist
flag
neck
wrist

Pad 6:
dress
golf
vest
belt
pants

Pad 7:
swing
sled
blocks
silk
drum

Pad 8:
tag
crab
golf
Ping Pong
kick ball

Pad 9:
skip
step
Brad
stop
jump

9

spin	glass	(last)	stem	track
gloss	Scat	spin	skit	grab
crab	went	asked	crib	trick

● Fill in the shaded boxes with words from the top box.

Hank is __last__ in line.

l a s t

The plant has a long _____.

Fran _____ to bed at ten o'clock.

Lan Ming can _____ the top.

"_____, cat!" yelled Gran.

Halloween is _____ or treat time.

Mom drank a _____ of milk.

The baby slept in a _____.

"Can you help me?" _____ the twin.

● Write the shaded letters in the blanks below to solve the puzzle.

"If you _s_ ___ ___ ___ on a ___ ___ ___ ___ ___, you . . ."

10

Do you remember the **trick** for reading some longer words? Look for small words within big **compound words.**

handstand = hand + stand
w   w

drumstick = drum + stick
w   w

● Put **w** and **w** under the 2 **small words** in each **compound word**. Then draw a line between the 2 small words. Read them.

hand stand	handbag	anthill
w w		
dumptruck	sandbox	grabbag
blacktop	sandhill	windmill
itself	drumstick	stepmom
himself	milkman	dustmop
dogsled	fanbelt	sandman

The Quinns are going camping by a pond. Help them make a list of **what to pack** and **what to do** before they go.

● Pick 12 words and phrases from the box to write on the list.

DO

1. scrub the stove
2.
3.
4.
5.
6.

PACK

1.
2.
3.
4.
5.
6.

knot the camp

scrub the stove

big, strong tent

rinse the sink

find the knapsacks

camping stove

raft

mend Stan's pants

travel clock

fold the tent

knapsacks

spill the plums

cut the grass

knock the test

sleeping bags

Sometimes 2 consonants make 1 sound: these are **consonant digraphs**.

ch
chin

sh
shell

th
thin

ph
gra**ph**

● Fill in the blanks with **ch**, **sh**, **th**, or **ph**.

___ ess

ca ___ ___

___ ___ip

Be ___ ___

di ___ ___

___ ___ell

___ ___ick

___ ___op

___ ___il

ben ___ ___

Se ___ ___

ran ___ ___

___ ___one

___ ___elf

___ ___em

pa ___ ___

● Fill in the blanks with words from the top box.

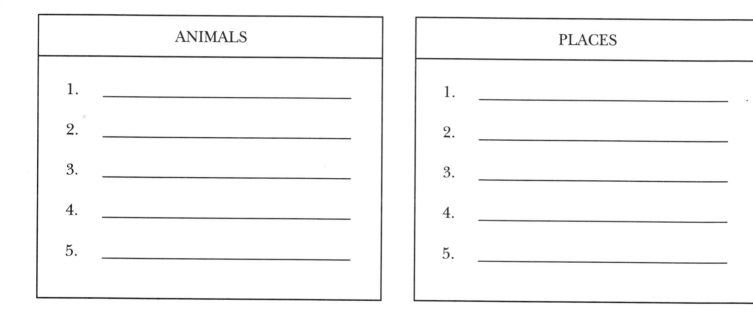

Go Fish	golf	splash	chum
thud	chess	hand	top shelf
shop	chest	fish	checkers
chimp	fresh	wrist	hopscotch
moth	shed	shin	Scotland
chin	ranch	chick	dolphin

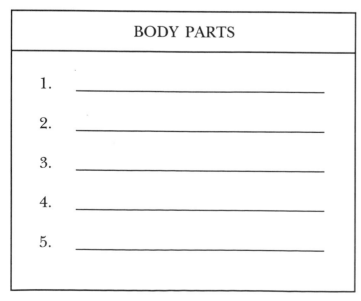

ANIMALS

1. _____
2. _____
3. _____
4. _____
5. _____

PLACES

1. _____
2. _____
3. _____
4. _____
5. _____

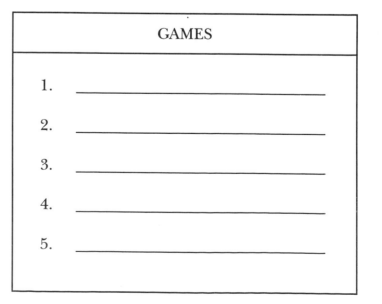

BODY PARTS

1. _____
2. _____
3. _____
4. _____
5. _____

GAMES

1. _____
2. _____
3. _____
4. _____
5. _____

Math	Lunch	Fish	Trash	Sinks	fishing
Bath	Ranch	Hush	Fudge	Brush	Catching

● Fill in the blanks with words from the top box.

Comb and _____ *set*

No hunting or _____

Kitchen _____ $25 off

_____ Tubs ON SALE!

_____ $2.00 a batch

Ox Ridge _____

_____ $3.75 Fish and Chips $2.80 Sandwiches

_____ Problems to Solve

_____ *Cans with Lids (20-gallon)*

_____ *Tank $20*

15

Here is another **trick** for reading longer words. If you can't find 2 small words, look for **2 consonants** in the middle of the long word.

I will cut between the 2 consonants in the middle of the word.

MAGIC SHOW

A syllable is a part of a word that has a sounded vowel. It is like a "beat" in a word.

Then you have 2 small **syllables** to read

hap | pen
c   c

happen = hap + pen
              c   c

dentist = den + tist
              c   c

● Put **c c** under the 2 **middle consonants** in each word. Then draw a line between the two consonants to divide the word into syllables.

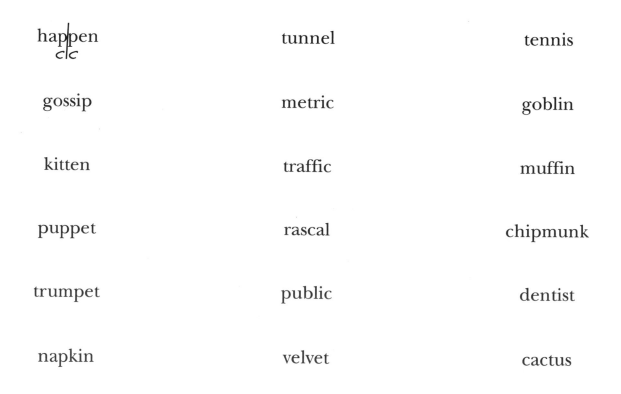

hap|pen c c	tunnel	tennis
gossip	metric	goblin
kitten	traffic	muffin
puppet	rascal	chipmunk
trumpet	public	dentist
napkin	velvet	cactus

● Pick 5 words from the words on page 16 and put each in a sentence.

1. _____

_____

_____

2. _____

_____

_____

3. _____

_____

_____

4. _____

_____

_____

5. _____

_____

_____

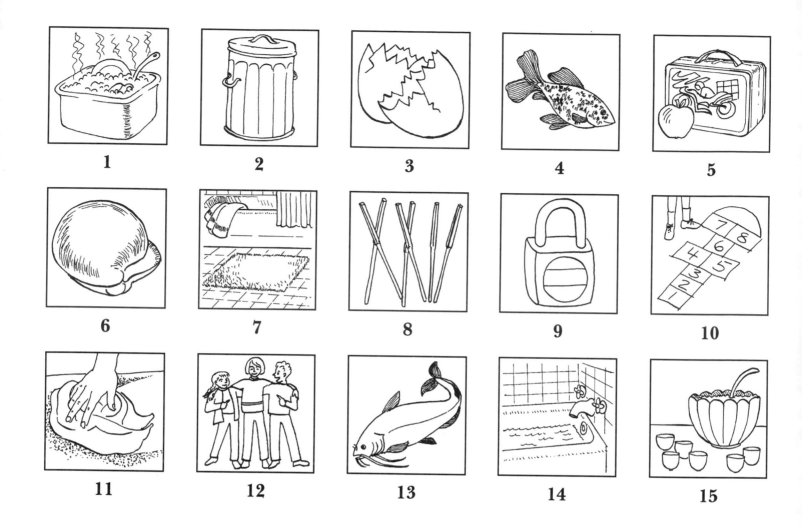

1   2   3   4   5

6   7   8   9   10

11   12   13   14   15

● Put **w** and **w** under the two small words in each compound word. Divide between them. Then number each word to match its picture.

__8__ chop|sticks

_____ goldfish

_____ clamshell

_____ lunchbox

_____ dustrag

_____ bathtub

_____ dishpan

_____ catfish

_____ trashcan

_____ eggnog

_____ eggshell

_____ themselves

_____ hopscotch

_____ bathmat

_____ padlock

18

● Make plurals by adding **s** or **es** to the underlined words.

Sept. 13, 1995

○ English

1. The child has lots of _block_____ .

2. There are six _path_____ in the woods.

3. We had ten Math _quizz_____ .

○ 4. Junko got new _glass_____ .

5. Look at the baby _fox_____ .

6. I see lots of _bench_____ in the park.

In most words, we add **s** to show **plural** (more than one).

In words ending with **s**, **x**, **z**, **ch**, and **sh** we add **es** to show plural.

We add **'s** to show **possession** or **ownership**.

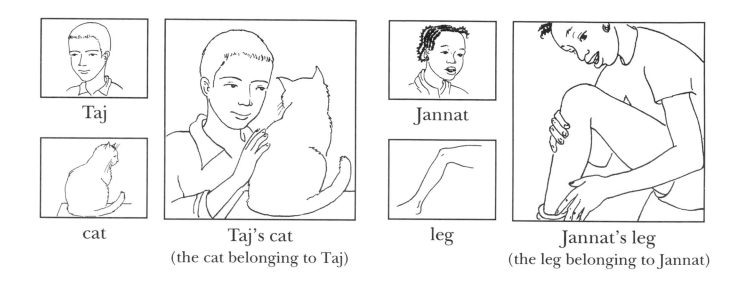

Taj

cat

Taj's cat
(the cat belonging to Taj)

Jannat

leg

Jannat's leg
(the leg belonging to Jannat)

● Circle **more than one** or **belonging to** for each underlined word.

1. Ten <u>eggs</u> hatched today.   (more than one, belonging to)

2. <u>Dad's</u> pen fell on the rug.   (more than one, belonging to)

3. <u>Abdul's</u> bag is on the bus.   (more than one, belonging to)

4. The <u>bugs</u> were buzzing at the picnic.   (more than one, belonging to)

5. <u>Mom's</u> cuff got wet in the sink.   (more than one, belonging to)

6. We had hot dogs with <u>buns</u>.   (more than one, belonging to)

7. <u>Kristin's</u> gum stuck to the desk.   (more than one, belonging to)

8. The tan duck is <u>Bem's</u>.   (more than one, belonging to)

9. The <u>hens</u> pecked in the pen.   (more than one, belonging to)

10. <u>Patwin's</u> ring is in the box.   (more than one, belonging to)

20

● Pick the best word to complete each sentence. Write it in the blank.

1. Dillon washed the ___**dishes**___ in the sink.
   (dish's, dishes)

2. The _____ gold is stacked in a locked box.
   (king's, kings)

3. "You get three _____," said the elf.
   (wish's, wishes)

4. Ellen was sick with the _____.
   (mump's, mumps)

5. The kids met _____ boss in the shop.
   (Mom's, Moms)

6. Zeb got ten _____ in the gash in his leg.
   (stitch's, stitches)

7. _____ neck got red in the sun.
   (Britt's, Britts)

8. The damp log got _____ pants wet.
   (Hassan's, Hassans)

9. The dog hid _____ slippers under the bed.
   (Dad's, Dads)

10. Paz played golf with his _____ golf clubs.
    (sister's, sisters)

11. Wen Lin likes to wear pants more than _____.
    (dress's, dresses)

12. The _____ fell off the pizza truck.
    (box's, boxes)

Watch out! These are trick questions!

● Here are some problems to solve. Think carefully.

It is Thanksgiving Day.

Dad is washing the dishes.

Seth is helping Dad by drying them.

There are 15 plates and 14 glasses to wash.

The suds are slippery, and Dad drops 2 glasses.

They crack, so Dad throws them into the trash.

The rest of the dishes are still in the sink.

A. How many dishes does Dad have left to dry?
B. Why?

Dad has _____ dishes left to dry because

_____

Themba has 2 bushes.

Each bush has 2 branches.

Each branch has a nest on it.

There are 2 eggs in each nest.

A. If all the eggs hatch, how many chicks will there be in all?
B. Why?

There will be _____ chicks in all because _____

_____

[Zero. Hens don't lay eggs in bushes.]

[Zero. Seth was drying the dishes.]

22

There are 2 times when vowels are **long** and "say their names":

1. When the only vowel in a word is at the end, it **says its name**.

    Trick: The vowel is falling off the cliff, so it calls its name.

2. When a syllable has 2 vowels, the 1st vowel says it name, and the 2nd is silent.

    Trick: The 1st vowel tells its name to the 2nd vowel.

When a word has just 1 vowel, but the vowel is **not** at the end, it does **not** say its name. Then the vowel is **short**.

● Write:

cap	tub	quack	tube	kit
quake	robe	slick	smock	slice
smoke	rob	Pete	plan	cub
cape	pet	plane	hi	cube

23

● Where do the words in the box belong?

King	rob	duck
cube	throne	duke
robe	cape	bed
grass	spin	snake
pine	mole	tadpole

BY A POND	IN A CASTLE
1. _____	1. _____
2. _____	2. _____
3. _____	3. _____
4. _____	4. _____
5. _____	5. _____
6. _____	6. _____

24

● Number the boxes so that they are in order.

_____ Then came the 2nd pitch. Fele missed that, too. "This is it," he said to himself. "If I hit the next ball, we win the game. If I miss, we lose."

_____ The kid on 2nd base got the ball, as Fele ran by 3rd base. He kept running to home plate.

___/___ The score was six to nine. Fele went up to bat. He said to himself, "We have 3 kids on base. If I make a home run, we will win the game."

_____ The 2nd baseman threw the ball. As the catcher put up his mitt to get it, Fele dove for home base. He made a home run!

_____ Fele missed the pitch. "Strike 1," yelled the umpire. Fele gripped the bat harder. "Come on," he said to himself.

_____ Fele hit the next ball, and it went up, up and landed by the fence. The 3 kids ran around the bases to home plate. Fele ran to 1st, then 2nd and 3rd base.

Do you remember the **tricks** for reading some longer words? Cut them up!

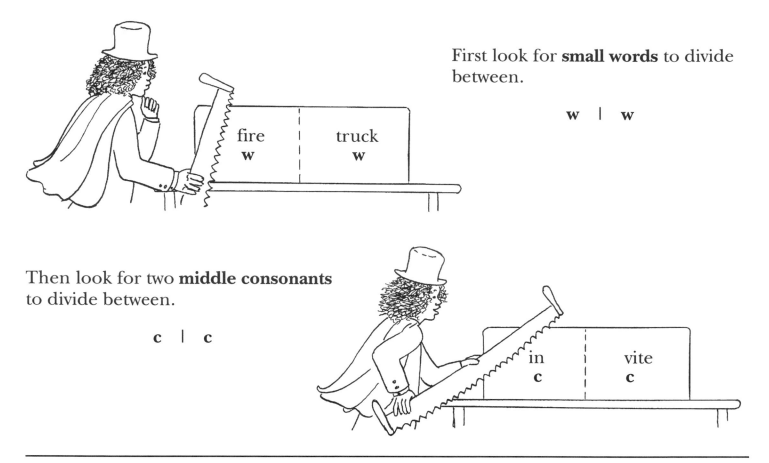

First look for **small words** to divide between.

w | w

Then look for two **middle consonants** to divide between.

c | c

● Look for 2 **small words** or **middle consonants** in each word. Mark them **w w** or **c c**, and divide into syllables. (Some words may be both.) Read the words.

fire|truck
w   w

sunrise

bathrobe

in|vite
c c

homemade

mistake

vampire

bedside

inside

campfire

injure

pancakes

pretzel

backbone

spaceship

backfire

homesick

admire

● Use the words from page 26 to fill in the blanks.

1. Those muffins are _____ by my stepmother.

2. Luce got _____ at camp and wanted to go home.

3. I hope to ride in a _____ some day.

4. Do you like butter on your _____?

5. Dun Nan wore his _____ to bed.

6. The snake was _____ a cage at the zoo.

7. We got up at five o'clock to watch the _____.

8. Wanda is going to _____ Matzu home for lunch.

9. The kids picked up sticks to make a _____.

10. "The hot _____ tastes yummy," said Viv.

11. A mammal has a _____, or a spine.

12. It's O.K. to make a _____.

13. My kitten sat by my _____ when I was sick.

14. The children _____ their grandfather.

Consonants are all the letters except *a, e, i, o,* and *u.*

Most consonants have just one sound.

But C has 2 sounds.

Most of the time C has the K sound.

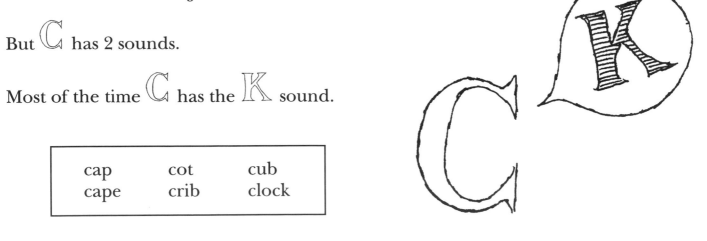

cap	cot	cub
cape	crib	clock

But C sounds like S when followed by *e, i,* or *y:*

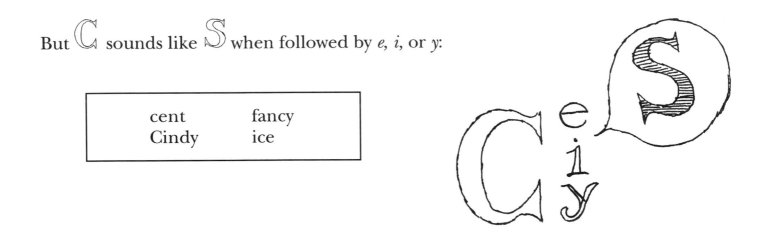

cent	fancy
Cindy	ice

● Circle each **c** in the words below. Write a **k** or **s** for the sound of each **c**.

s
(c)ent

club

plastic

correct

rice

fence

crest

lace

cab

fancy

contest

place

pencil

nice

cone

came

Grace

collect

price

carrots

cat

crib

cuff

picnic

28

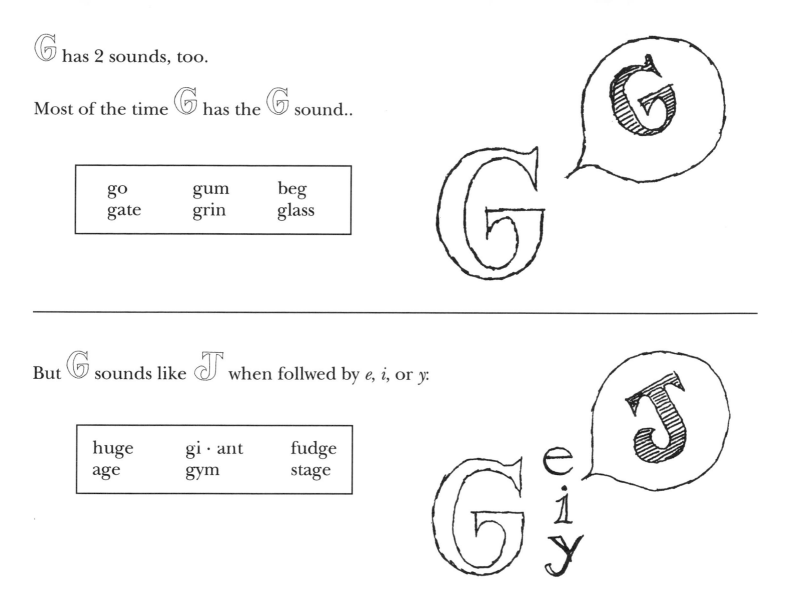

G has 2 sounds, too.

Most of the time G has the G sound..

go	gum	beg
gate	grin	glass

But G sounds like J when follwed by *e, i,* or *y:*

huge	gi · ant	fudge
age	gym	stage

● Circle each **g** in the words below. Write a **g** or **j** for the sound of each **g**.

huge	gypsy	smudge	stage
grape	globe	gallon	gust
ridge	page	gotten	gull
gas	gave	beg	guppy
golf	gadget	glasses	piglet
gym	age	gem	Gene

● Cross out the word on each pad that does not belong.

cub	face	gas
mice	leg	fudge
race	nose	rice
pig	cone	grapes
dog	chin	cake

nine	pencil	huge
ten	globe	big
cage	pen	wide
five	maps	hug
six	cute	thick

gate	can	cost
twice	bag	price
log	jug	age
grass	Grace	cents
fence	mug	sale

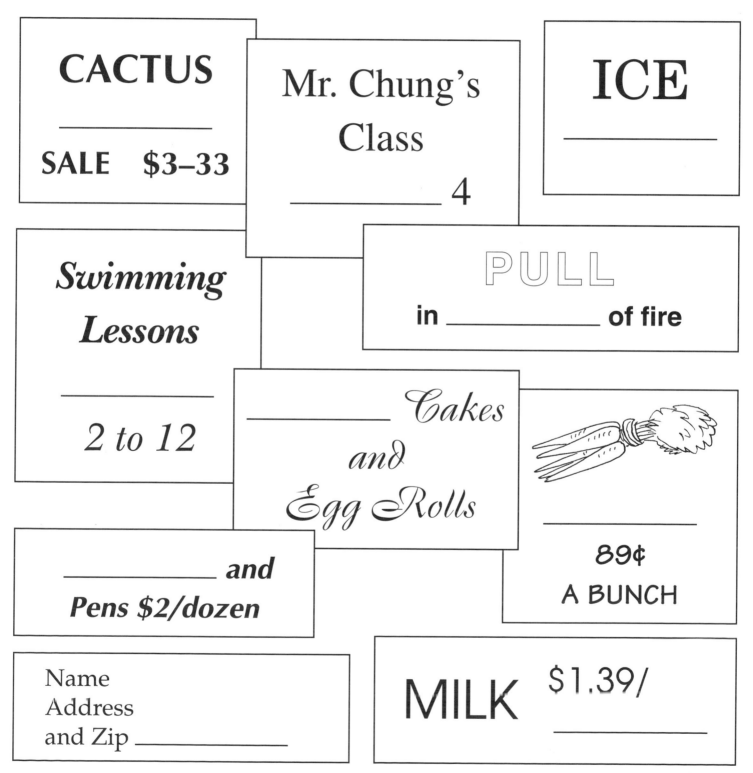

Ages   case   CUBES   Carrots   Pencils   Grade

PLANTS   Globe   Code   Cent   Gallon   Rice

● Fill in the blanks with words from the top box.

CACTUS

_____

SALE $3–33

Mr. Chung's Class

_____ 4

ICE

_____

Swimming Lessons

_____

2 to 12

PULL

in _____ of fire

_____ *Cakes and Egg Rolls*

_____

89¢

A BUNCH

_____ **and Pens $2/dozen**

Name
Address
and Zip _____

MILK $1.39/

_____

The kids went on a **Scavenger Hunt** to find the things on this list.

● Check off the things the children found.

Hunt
bone
boxtop
rock
pretzel
five cents
eggshell
rope
tack

Bridget got a wishbone from a chicken her mom baked.

Abdul got a nickel from his stepdad.

Frances got the top of a box of pretzels and a thumbtack from her mom's desk.

Vincent picked up a stone from the sidewalk.

Lance got the shell from a cracked egg.

Asha got a bit of twine from the shed.

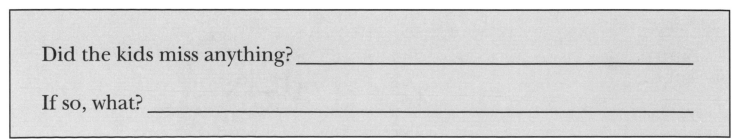

Did the kids miss anything? _____

If so, what? _____

32

Some words take a short cut by leaving out some letters. These words are called **contractions**. **Contract** means to get smaller.

For example,

I've	=	I have
it's	=	it is, it has
can't	=	can not
we'll	=	we will
let's	=	let us

The **apostrophe** (') takes the place of the missing letters.

● Write the two words that each underlined contraction stands for:

It's time to go to the dentist. _____

I'll meet you on the front steps. _____

What's taking you so long? _____

I've been waiting for ages. _____

You'll make us late. _____

Don't stop to put on your coat. _____

I can't wait any longer. _____

We're going to be late. _____

I'm mad, and the dentist will be, too. _____

She's a good dentist. _____

Let's go! _____

When a word has 2 vowels, the 1st vowel usually says its name, and the 2nd vowel is silent:

Trick: The 1st vowel tells its name to the 2nd vowel.

● Pick 3 words from the box to complete each sentence.

1. I can _____ the _____ on

   my _____.

2. _____ sits in the best _____ in the

   last _____.

3. Rashid has on a _____ and a _____

   _____ he got from his dad.

4. The wind makes a _____ _____ go,

   but you use _____ to make a rowboat go.

5. _____ _____ at the desk to

   _____ her bill.

| cheeks |
| rain |
| lie |
| feel |

| row |
| seat |
| ray |
| Joan |

| tie |
| bow |
| tea |
| suit |

| boat |
| sail |
| seal |
| oars |

| waits |
| pay |
| Sue |
| say |

● Aleem has things to do. Help him make his **shopping** and **cleaning** list.
Use words or phrases of words from the box to write on the list.

Shopping

Get 1. _____
2. _____
3. _____
4. _____
5. _____
6. _____

Cleaning

Wash 1. _____
2. _____
3. _____
4. _____
5. _____
6. _____

pie crust

kitchen floor

kitchen ceiling

blue jay

cheese

peanuts

stairs

steers

bathtub

rescue

fruit juice

ice cream

sparrow

windows

peaches

stove

● Fill in the blanks with words from the top box.

gray	quail	weird	three o'clock
sparrow	Faith	leash	three years
elbow	today	yellow	keychain
bowl	green	repeat	blue jay
tray	crow	Tuesday	pulley
Sunday	white	blue	peacock

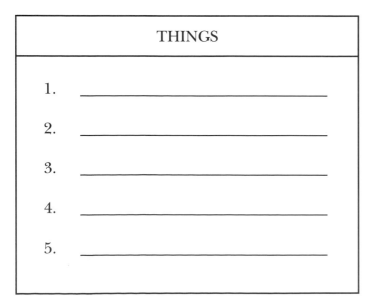

BIRDS

1. _____

2. _____

3. _____

4. _____

5. _____

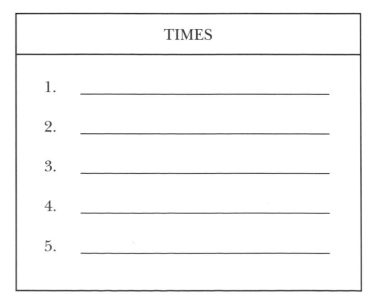

COLORS

1. _____

2. _____

3. _____

4. _____

5. _____

THINGS

1. _____

2. _____

3. _____

4. _____

5. _____

TIMES

1. _____

2. _____

3. _____

4. _____

5. _____

Flow	Mail	Street	May	RAILROAD	Cream
LOAD	Day	each	Key	Earrings	wheel

● Fill in the blanks with the words from the box.

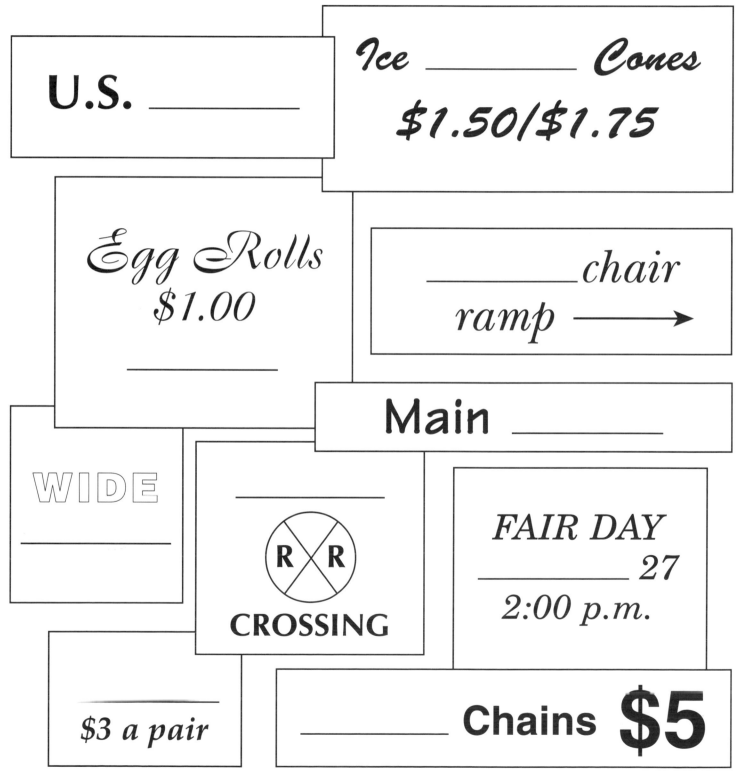

U.S. _____

Ice _____ Cones
$1.50/$1.75

Egg Rolls
$1.00
_____

_____*chair*
ramp ⟶

Main _____

WIDE
_____

_____
R ⨯ R
CROSSING

FAIR DAY
_____ *27*
2:00 p.m.

_____
$3 a pair

_____ Chains **$5**

flea	roast	raise	juice	bowl
true	bleak	Keith	tried	weird
flow	kneel	clue	throw	blow

● Fill in the shaded boxes with words from the top box.

Kaylene _____ to float, but she can't.   ___ ___ ▨ ___ ___

We_____ on our knees.   ___ ▨ ___ ___ ___

If the winds _____, the sailboat will go.   ▨ ___ ___ ___

Is that sentence _____ or false?   ___ ▨ ___ ___

We ate _____ beef last Sunday.   ___ ___ ▨ ___ ___

"Please _____ your hand," said the teacher.   ___ ___ ▨ ___ ___

Streams _____ downhill.   ___ ▨ ___ ___

Neil spied a _____ on his kitten.   ___ ▨ ___ ___

_____ sneezed on his clean gray suit.   ___ ▨ ___ ___ ___

● Write the shaded letters in the blanks below to solve the puzzle.

Caitlin is blind, so she cannot see. How does she read?

She reads ___ ___   ___ ___ ___ ___ ___ ___ ___.

38

Plurals do not always follow the rules:

1. Some words ending in **f** and **fe** form the plural by changing to **ves**.

Examples:

elf	—— elves	life	—— lives	leaf	—— leaves
self	—— selves	wife	—— wives	loaf	—— loaves
shelf	—— shelves	knife	—— knives		

2. More than one man = **men**. More than one woman = **women**.

● Fill in the spaces:

SINGULAR (ONE)	PLURAL (MORE THAN ONE)
wife	wives
life	*lives*
	knivcs
leaf	
	selves
elf	
shelf	
man	
	women

● Write the best word to complete each sentence. Write it in the blank.

Mee Yon and Hee Kwan raked _____ into a pile.
(leaf, leaves)

Bem painted three _____ green.
(shelf, shelves)

Jim's wife cut the cake with a _____.
(knife, knives)

Neil crossed the street by him_____.
(self, selves)

Five _____ danced on the green leaf.
(elf, elves)

We add **'s** to show possession by one owner.

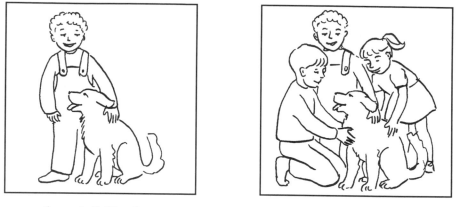

the child's dog   the club's dog

We add **'** to show belonging to more than one owner (with plural ending in **s** or **es**).

the kids' parrot   the kid's parrot

● Circle the word to complete each sentence.

1. The _____ home was crushed by the bulldozer.
   (ants, ants')

2. Ms. Lime wrote _____ name on a list.
   (Simons, Simon's)

3. The _____ rice fell off their chopsticks.
   (kids, kids')

4. The _____ van had a flat tire.
   (Joneses, Joneses')

5. That gray kitten is _____.
   (Graces, Grace's)

6. The _____ faces were made of bone.
   (puppets, puppets')

● Neema dropped her story on the bus. Help her put the pages back in order by numbering them.

---

page [1]

Neema Kimani
May 22, 1999

A Day with Spot

When I was three years old we got a beagle. A beagle is a breed of dog. On the next

---

page [ ]

away. He got out when my dad was getting the mail from the mail man.

Dad and I ran to catch him. But he

---

page [ ]

"He went that way!" yelled Mr. Lee.
Then he knocked over Ms. Reid and spilled her shopping bags. "He went that way!" she screamed.

Then we saw Spot at

---

page [ ]

the store. He was wagging his tail. The storekeeper was feeding him. I put his leash on and took him home. Dad helped Ms. Reid with her things.
The next day, Dad paid Mr. Lee for the paint. When the mailman comes, we keep Spot on a leash.

---

page [ ]

page you can see what my beagle looks like.

When my beagle was one year old he ran

---

page [ ]

disappeared! Then we heard a man moaning, "Oh, no!"

We ran down the alley to see Mr. Lee lying in the street with a paintbrush and a spilled bucket of paint.

41

Here is another **trick** for reading longer words. If you can't find **2 small words** or **2 middle consonants** in the longer word, then look for **1 middle consonant**.

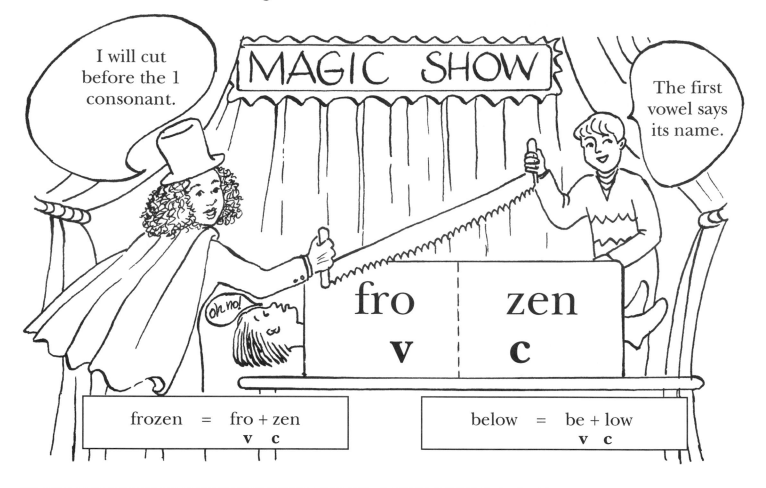

I will cut before the 1 consonant.

MAGIC SHOW

The first vowel says its name.

oh no!

fro zen
v   c

frozen = fro + zen
         v   c

below = be + low
        v   c

● Put **v c** under the **first vowel** and **middle consonant** in each word. Then draw a line before the middle consonant to divide the word into syllables. Read the words.

fro|zen v c	before	zebra
hero	below	decay
moment	recent	spoken
solo	decide	below
spiral	minus	zero
recess	hotel	pilot

SOLVE the RIDDLES

● Try to solve the riddles yourself or find the answers in the mixed-up list below. Write the letter on the line.

1. How many hairs in a quail's tail? _____

2. How many hairs in a deer's tail? _____

3. Why is the letter *D* like a goat? _____

4. When is a baby like a cup? _____

5. Why is the letter *S* like a dog? _____

6. Why does a dog wag its tail? _____

7. If a yellow stone fell into the Red Sea, what would happen? _____
   _____

8. Why are a trap and a cold alike? _____

9. When is a boat like a heap of snow? _____

10. Who sits before the queen with his hat on? _____

_____

a. Because it will make cat scat.

b. The coachman.

c. They are both catching.

d. Because you cannot have a kid without it.

e. Zero. Quails have feathers, not hair.

f. When it is teething (tea thing).

g. It would get wet.

h. When it is adrift (a drift).

i. Because it wants to.

j. Zero. The hairs are on the tail, not in it.

Y is confused . . .

At the beginning of a word or syllable, she sounds like herself.

This is **y** as a **consonant**.

But much of the time **y** thinks she is **i**:

She sounds like long-i,

This is one of **y**'s long sounds.

. . . or short-i.

This is **y**'s short sound.

At the end of longer words, she acts like long-e.

This is **y**'s other long sound.

gym	spy	Bryce	Yellowstone Lake
bunny	Yutu	Lynn	year
lady	sky	yell	ladybug
kitty	Yo	puppy	canyon
pony	yak	city	pigsty

● Fill in the blanks with words from the top box.

y = y	y = ĭ	y = ē
1. _____	1. _____	1. _____
2. _____	2. _____	2. _____
3. _____	**y = ī**	3. _____
4. _____	1. _____	4. _____
5. _____	2. _____	5. _____
6. _____	3. _____	6. _____
7. _____	4. _____	7. _____

● Fill in the blanks with words from the top box.

ANIMALS	PEOPLE	PLACES
1. _____	1. _____	1. _____
2. _____	2. _____	2. _____
3. _____	3. _____	3. _____
4. _____	4. _____	4. _____
5. _____	5. _____	5. _____
6. _____	6. _____	6. _____

When adding an ending to a word ending in **y**, change the **y** to **i**.

cry + **ed** = cr**ied**	cry + **es** = cr**ies**
funny + **er** = funn**ier**	funny + **es** = funn**ies**
fry + **ed** = fr**ied**	fry + **es** = fr**ies**

But don't change the **y** when:

1. adding **ing**
2. the base word has a vowel before the **y**.

play + **ed** = play**ed**	play + **s** = play**s**
play + **ing** = play**ing**	cry + **ing** = cry**ing**
toy + **ing** = toy**ing**	toy + **s** = toy**s**

● Fill in the blanks.

Word	+ ing	+ s/es	+ ed
play			
try		tries	
key	——		——
yell			
cry			cried
say			said
donkey	——		——
stay			
fly			——

The children have a **yearbook**.

● Fill in the blanks with words from the list.

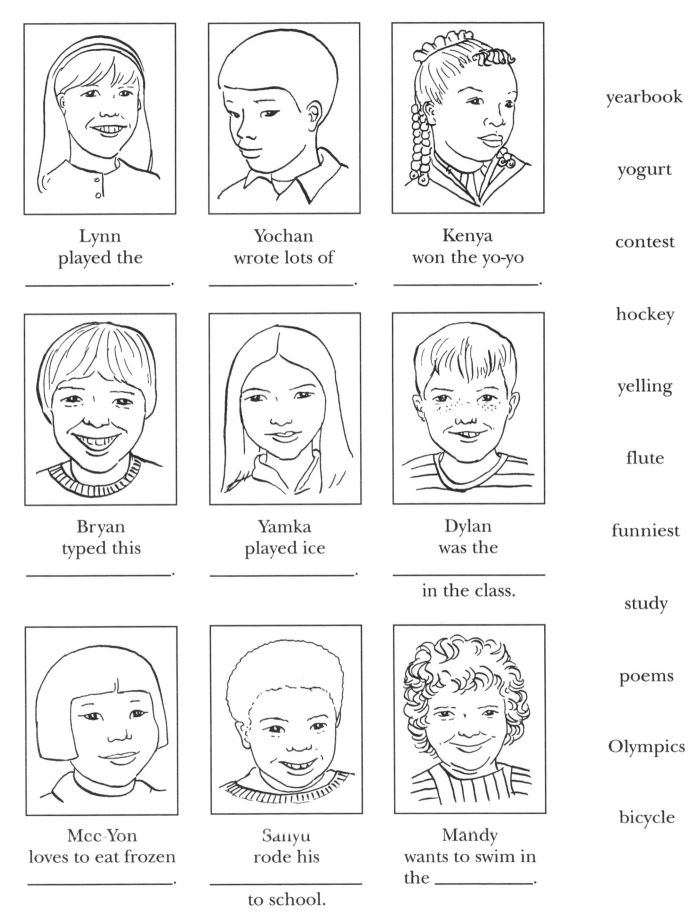

Lynn
played the
_____.

Yochan
wrote lots of
_____.

Kenya
won the yo-yo
_____.

Bryan
typed this
_____.

Yamka
played ice
_____.

Dylan
was the
_____
in the class.

Mee-Yon
loves to eat frozen
_____.

Sanyu
rode his
_____
to school.

Mandy
wants to swim in
the _____.

yearbook

yogurt

contest

hockey

yelling

flute

funniest

study

poems

Olympics

bicycle

Puppy   Pony   Flurries   Fries   Crying   Gym

Guppies   Style   Fairy   Jelly   Flying   Pair

● Fill in the blanks with words from the top box.

Chopsticks

$2 for

a _____

_____

OPEN

Weekdays

9 to 6

Weekends

10 to 5

KITE _____

CONTEST

_____ *Tale*

Puppet Show

2:00 Today

_____

Rides

$5

Free _____

with leash and

bowl.

Has had shots.

_____

with

Tank

Chance of snow

_____, high 31°

Hot Dogs $1.50

French _____ $ .99

Fried Yams $ .99

Grape _____

● Write **true** or **false** after each sentence.

Fairies and elves are ponies. _____

A dime is ten pennies. _____

A week is longer than a year. _____

Glue is stickier than ten pennies. _____

Ice is not frozen. _____

Twenty is much more than sixty. _____

A myth tells what really happened. _____

The sun is up in the daytime. _____

To be jolly is to be happy. _____

A gym is a place you can swim in. _____

If you run quickly, you are fast. _____

Subways are flying in the air. _____

May comes before June. _____

Babies can tell time on a clock. _____

You can type on jelly. _____

When a vowel is followed by **r**, the **r** changes the sound of the vowel.

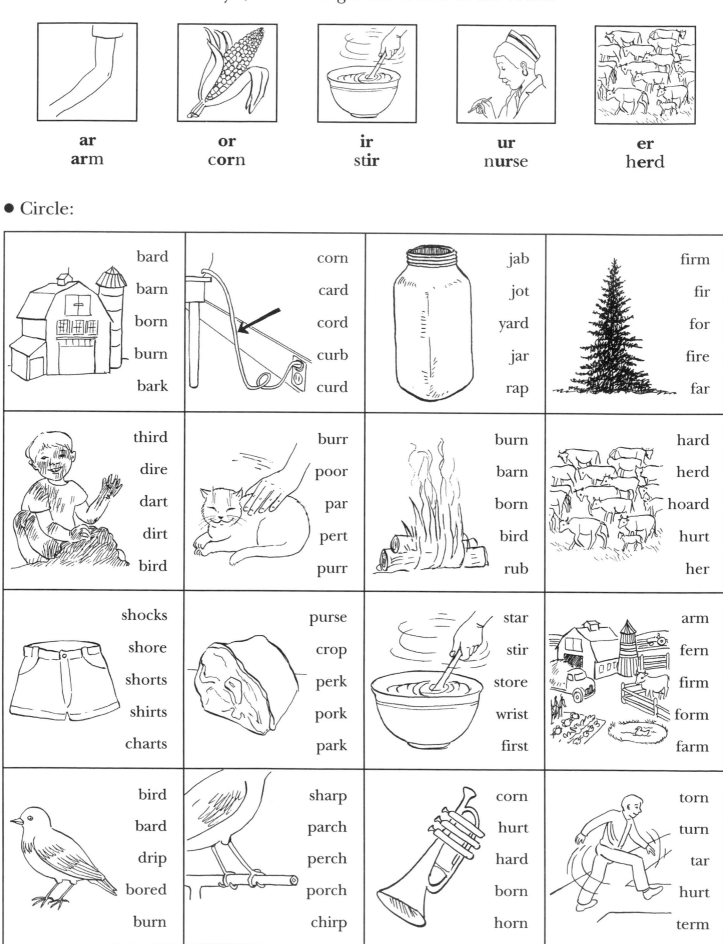

ar	**or**	**ir**	**ur**	**er**
arm	c**or**n	st**ir**	n**ur**se	h**er**d

● Circle:

bard / barn / born / burn / bark	corn / card / cord / curb / curd	jab / jot / yard / jar / rap	firm / fir / for / fire / far
third / dire / dart / dirt / bird	burr / poor / par / pert / purr	burn / barn / born / bird / rub	hard / herd / hoard / hurt / her
shocks / shore / shorts / shirts / charts	purse / crop / perk / pork / park	star / stir / store / wrist / first	arm / fern / firm / form / farm
bird / bard / drip / bored / burn	sharp / parch / perch / porch / chirp	corn / hurt / hard / born / horn	torn / turn / tar / hurt / term

50

er is an ending that can be added to words.

It can mean **a person who** . . .

run — runn**er**
sing — sing**er**
fly — fli**er**

er can also mean **more** . . .

clean — clean**er**
big — bigg**er**
tricky — tricki**er**

● Add **er** to the words in the box to help Nora finish her letter.

pitch	short
hard	fast
long	teach
thirsty	help

er

Saturday, Sept. 7

Dear Jabbar,

School started. (I am in third grade.) It is _____ than last year. My _____ is nice. I will be her _____ next Thursday.

I like sports. My legs are _____ so I can run _____. I am the _____ in baseball.

I hope you like sixth grade.

Your pal,
Nora

● Cross out the word on each pad that does not belong:

shorts	fern	purple
shirt	fork	dark blue
scarf	flower	car
scar	birch tree	orange
skirt	fir tree	silver

corn	under	winter
pork	mother	summer
popcorn	father	fall
tortillas	sister	turban
sort	brother	spring

Saturn	starfish	arm
Germ	swordfish	farm
Jupiter	horse	park
Mars	shark	barn
Mercury	sea urchin	yard

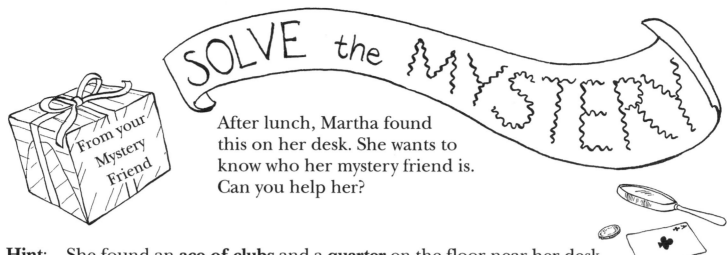

SOLVE the MYSTERY

After lunch, Martha found this on her desk. She wants to know who her mystery friend is. Can you help her?

From your Mystery Friend

Hint: She found an **ace of clubs** and a **quarter** on the floor near her desk.

Was it Arturo?

Arturo charged his lunch. After lunch he played marbles in the corner.

Was it Mr. Roberto?

Mr. Roberto, the teacher, lets the kids play cards after lunch. During lunch, he worked on report cards.

Was it Nora?

Nora gave the teacher a dollar for lunch. She hates to play cards.

Was it Kirsten?

Kirsten paid 25¢ for milk at lunch. But it costs thirteen cents, so she got back some change.

Was it Ari?

Ari likes to keep a deck of cards in his pocket. He lost a quarter before lunch.

Was it Darcy?

Darcy gave her four quarters to Mr. Roberto for lunch this morning. When she played cards with Ari, they were missing a card.

● Who gave Martha the box? _____

How can you tell? _____

_____

her parents couldn't afford it. Then one March morning

Do you remember the **tricks** for reading longer words? Cut them up!

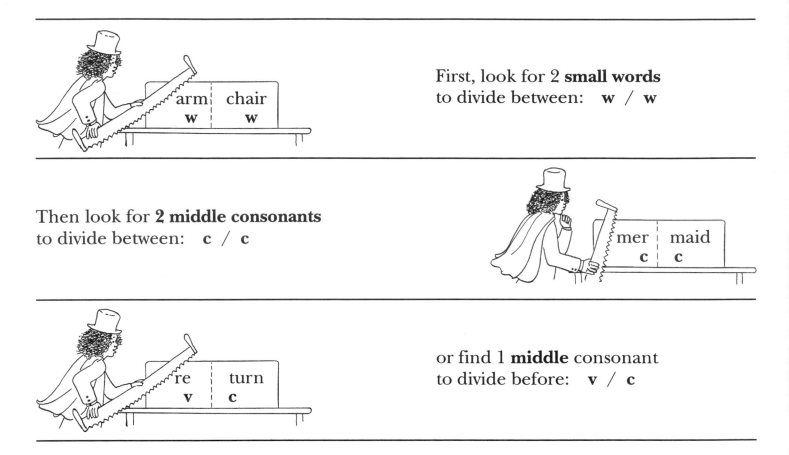

First, look for 2 **small words**
to divide between: **w / w**

Then look for **2 middle consonants**
to divide between: **c / c**

or find 1 **middle** consonant
to divide before: **v / c**

● Look for **2 small words**, **2 middle consonants**, or a **first vowel** and **1 middle** consonant
to divide between. Mark them **w w**, **c c**, or **v c** and divide between them. Read the words.

return	gerbil	corner
pepper	turban	major
report	rainstorm	birdbath
birthday	fever	thirty
charcoal	flavor	reverse
clover	quarter	minor

Sometimes 2 vowels together make a sound unlike either of them makes alone.

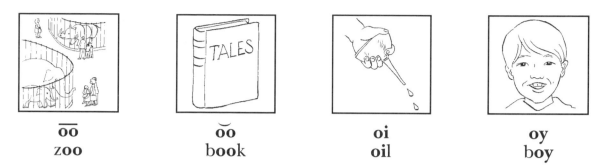

$\overline{oo}$
zoo

$\breve{oo}$
book

oi
oil

oy
b**oy**

● Fill in the blanks with **oo**, **oi**, or **oy**. Use **oy** (not **oi**) at the end of a word.

p __ __ l

f __ __ d

R __ __

n __ __ se

c __ __ kies

s __ __ l

sp __ __ n

__ __ nk

m __ __ se

j __ __

w __ __ d

p __ __ nt

p __ __ son

t __ __

r __ __ m

h __ __ k

● Circle:

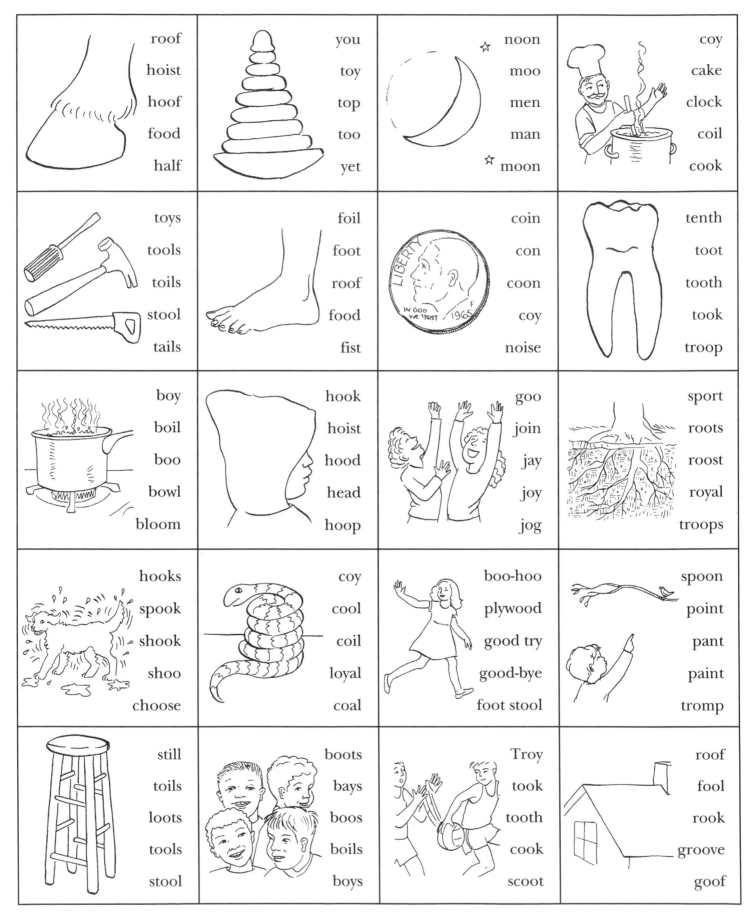

roof hoist hoof food half	you toy top too yet	☆ noon moo men man ☆ moon	coy cake clock coil cook
toys tools toils stool tails	foil foot roof food fist	coin con coon coy noise	tenth toot tooth took troop
boy boil boo bowl bloom	hook hoist hood head hoop	goo join jay joy jog	sport roots roost royal troops
hooks spook shook shoo choose	coy cool coil loyal coal	boo-hoo plywood good try good-bye foot stool	spoon point pant paint tromp
still toils loots tools stool	boots bays boos boils boys	Troy took tooth cook scoot	roof fool rook groove goof

58

● Help Oona make 2 lists: things to buy at the store, and jobs to do when she gets back. Pick words from the box to write on the list.

To Get at the Store

1.
2.
3.
4.
5.
6.
7.

To Do

1.
2.
3.
4.
5.
6.
7.
8.

toothbrushes

ointment

sweep the dining room

moo at the balloons

glue the tool box

large spoons

cook dinner

change oil in car

goo

motor oil

wood glue

clean the kitchen sink

cat food

good kids' book

feed the cat

boil the yams

zoom and shoo

brush my teeth

woof-woof

tooth fairy	WOOL	Hoops	snooze	POISON	Spoons
toothbrush	scoop	Foot	TOOLS	Hooks	wood

● Fill in the blanks with words from the top box.

_____ SUIT $70

1 FREE _____ with purchase of toothpaste

Hula _____

Knives, Forks, and _____ $5

BEWARE! _____

Ice Cream or Frozen Yogurt

1 _____ $1.50
2 scoops $1.75

10-_____ BOAT for SALE

Ply_____ Boards 4' × 8'

Fish _____ *and Rods*

HAMMERS, PLIERS, WRENCHES AND OTHER _____

60

Who makes these noises?

Boo!   Moo!   Cock-a-doodle-doo!

Boo-hoo!   Oops!   Oink-oink!

Toot! Toot!   Shoo!   Woof-woof!

● Fill in the balloons with the words from the top box.

● Who said it? Draw a line from the speaker to the right box.

The happy boy said,

"Where is my wooden spoon?"

The cook asked,

"This is a good book."

The spook yelled,

"Boo Hoo! Want more!"

The reader said,

"Boo to you!!"

The girl in the swimsuit asked,

"The filling in your tooth is smooth, now."

The boy with the coin said,

"I got it at Hiroya's birthday party."

It was time to go, so Floyd said,

"Where is the pool?"

The girl with the balloon said,

"I have a silver quarter."

The dentist said,

"Good-bye, Leroy!"

The baby cried,

"I'm in a good mood."

Here are some more vowels making a new sound together:

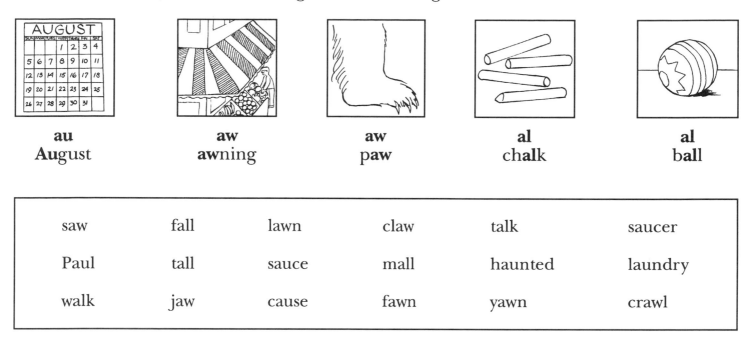

| **au** | **aw** | **aw** | **al** | **al** |
| August | awning | paw | chalk | ball |

saw	fall	lawn	claw	talk	saucer
Paul	tall	sauce	mall	haunted	laundry
walk	jaw	cause	fawn	yawn	crawl

● Write:

• Pick the best word to complete each sentence. Write it in the blank.

1. Anton felt _____ because he ate too many strawberries.
   (law, awesome, awful)

2. In the _____, leaves fall from the trees.
   (August, autumn, awning)

3. The test Laura took yesterday had true-_____ questions on it.
   (fault, fall, false)

4. When the play was over, the actors got _____ from the audience.
   (applause, sauce, autographs)

5. The baby cannot walk yet, but he can _____.
   (claw, crawl, chalk)

6. The warm sunshine made the ice on the pond _____.
   (talk, thaw, haunt)

7. Always use the _____ to cross the street safely.
   (small talk, sleepwalk, crosswalk)

8. Austin caught the _____ in his mom's mitt.
   (fly ball, mixing bowl, golf ball)

9. Walter got a _____ for his birthday.
   (close call, meat ball, bowling ball)

10. Laurel is going to camp in _____.
    (August, shawl, drawn)

64

● Fill in the blanks with words from the top box.

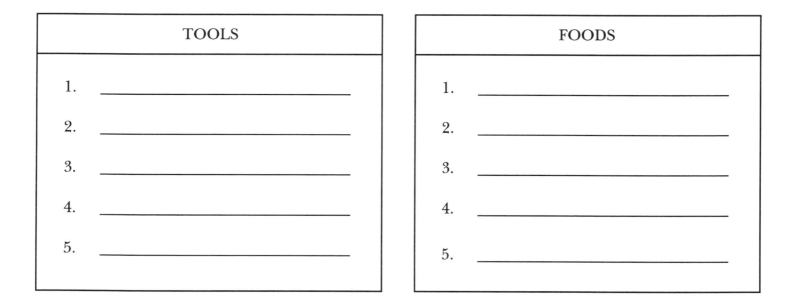

awl	hammer	lawn	chain saw
sauce	football	author	meatballs
mall	lawyer	drill	bank vault
aunt	fawn	hall	hand saw
salt	strawberry	hawk	cole slaw
Maura	yawn	Paulo	sidewalk

TOOLS

1. _____
2. _____
3. _____
4. _____
5. _____

FOODS

1. _____
2. _____
3. _____
4. _____
5. _____

PLACES

1. _____
2. _____
3. _____
4. _____
5. _____

PEOPLE

1. _____
2. _____
3. _____
4. _____
5. _____

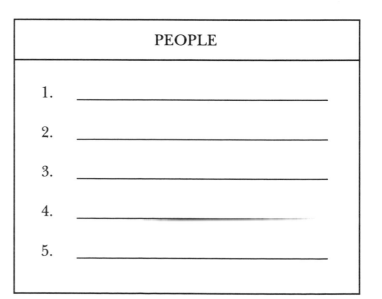

● Fill in the blanks with words from the top box.

Tomato
_____
69¢

Spaghetti + _____ $3.99

_____
Milk
Balls

_____
Game
at
2:00 p.m.

SQUEAKY
CLEAN
_____

CAMP
Summer-_____-Winter-Spring

Summer
rates
during
July &
_____
($5 off)

Pines
Shopping
_____

Please keep off
the _____

STOP   at
_____

Caw	her	launch	wall	sleepwalk
paw	fawn	boot	draw	haul
law	all	dawn	salty	waltz

● Fill in the shaded boxes with words from the top box.

The puppy shook hands with its _____. ___ ___

Maureen will _____ the straw to the barn. ___ ___ ___

Claude kicked off his _____. ___ ___ ___

The _____ paused, then sprang into the woods. ___ ___ ___

The mother hugged _____ daughter. ___ ___

The crow called, "_____" to its mate. ___ ___

At _____, we say that the sun rises. ___ ___ ___

Arturo's drawing is hanging on the _____. ___ ___ ___

The ham tastes too _____ . ___ ___ ___

● Write the shaded letters in the blanks below to solve the puzzle.

Paula got this from her Aunt Audrey. What did she get?

She got a ___ ___ ___ ___ ___ ___ ___ ___ ___.

● Use the **tricks** you know to divide these words into syllables. Then choose from these words to complete the sentences below.

toothbrush	rooster	Laurel
spooky	noisy	thunder
forget	bassoon	balloons
saucer	oyster	laundry
backyard	because	awful
even	enjoys	always

1. "Cock-a-doodle-doo!" crowed the _____ in the barnyard.

2. Maura had thirty _____ at her surprise birthday party.

3. Kareem said that the haunted house at the fair was _____.

4. Brook was tired _____ she had played football all day.

5. Hiro can't wait to brush his teeth with his new _____.

6. The kitten hid under the sofa when he heard the_____.

7. Leroy _____ horseback riding at his summer camp.

8. It was too _____ inside, so Dad went outside to read.

9. The Mars men landed in their flying _____.

10. "I will _____ love you," said Crystal, hugging her puppy.

11. Walt is learning to play the _____ in music class.

12. "The cole slaw tasted _____," claimed Una.

68

● Write **true** or **false** after each sentence.

First we went shopping at the mall. Then we ate golf balls in the hall. _____

It is good to walk on the sidewalk and cross the street at the crosswalk. _____

You can cook sauce in a saucepan on the stove. _____

Walter got a phone call from Jack in the Beanstalk. They had a
good talk. _____

The astronaut went on a spacewalk. She was floating in space. _____

Laurel got sunburned because she sat at the laundry too long. _____

In the autumn, the leaves turn red and yellow, and fall from the trees. _____

You can play football with snowballs. They stay frozen in the
August sun. _____

You can draw on the sidewalk with chalk. _____

The hall has walls on both sides. _____

A walnut grows on a tall cornstalk. _____

A hawk will play ball in a haunted stall. _____

Paul can haul the load home from the mall. _____

The fawn put on a shawl with five paws. _____

SOLVE the RIDDLES

● Try to solve the riddles yourself or find the answers in the mixed-up list below and write the letter on the line.

1. When is it easy to read in the woods? _____

2. When is a rope like a child at school? _____

3. What is a fawn after it is 1 year old? _____

4. If you go into a sausage factory, what smells the most? _____

5. Why did the lobster blush? _____

6. Why do birds fly south in the autumn? _____

7. Why is the letter F like a fish hook? _____

8. What did Paul Revere say when he finished his famous ride? _____

9. When is water like a tiger? _____

10. Why is a book like a king? _____

_____

a. When it is taut (taught).

b. Because it saw the salad dressing.

c. Because it has many pages.

d. Because it is too far to walk.

e. Two years old.

f. When it makes a spring.

g. When autumn turns the leaves.

h. Because it will make eel feel.

i. Whoa.

j. Your nose.

Here are some more vowels making a new sound together.

cloud   mouth   tower   bow

● Circle.

out chow ouch thou couch	caw coo coy cue cow	pawn proud prowl powder droop	towel tool tall toil trowel
soothe sauce sow south stout	mound mouth moose mount mouse	foul fowl flower floor falter	croon crown crone clown crowd
allowed load laud loot loud	drools boils bounce blouse blues	all awl owl wool howl	dawn down boon drown bound
ground goon gnaw gown growl	shower sour sawyer shouter surround	trout toot taught town treat	south shout snout shoot chows

trout	count	frown	growl
plow	shower	house	mountain
pouch	scout	brow	sunflower
pow-wow	aloud	pounds	campground
bounce	mouse	compound	

● Write:

_____	_____	_____	_____
_____	_____	_____	_____
_____	_____	_____	_____
_____	_____	_____	_____

● Where do the words in the box belong?

clown	barn	merry-go-round
balloons	crosswalk	firehouse
plow	grocery store	farmhouse
cotton candy	sidewalk	funhouse
bumper cars	cows	South Street
cornstalk	rooster	park bench

ON A FARM

1. _____
2. _____
3. _____
4. _____
5. _____
6. _____

AT A FAIR

1. _____
2. _____
3. _____
4. _____
5. _____
6. _____

IN A TOWN

1. _____
2. _____
3. _____
4. _____
5. _____
6. _____

showers	power	Sound	GROUND	Brownies	FOUND
Crown	TOWER	pound	allowed	South	hour

● Fill in the blanks with words from the top box.

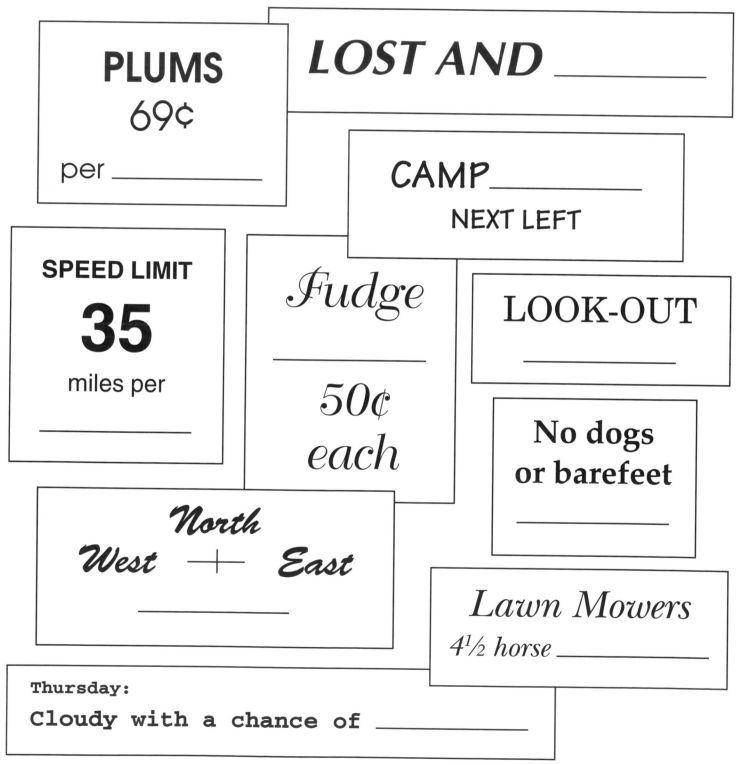

PLUMS
69¢

per _____

LOST AND _____

CAMP_____
NEXT LEFT

SPEED LIMIT
35
miles per
_____

Fudge
_____
50¢
each

LOOK-OUT
_____

**No dogs
or barefeet**
_____

North
West ── *East*
_____

Lawn Mowers
4½ horse _____

Thursday:
Cloudy with a chance of _____

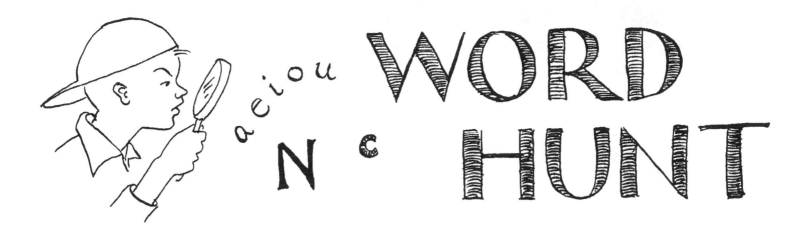

Clues: 1. It is a compound word. (A compound word is the name for a big word made up of 2 or more little words.)

2. Four of its letters are vowels. (The vowels are **a**, **e**, **i**, **o**, **u**, and sometimes **y** and **w**.)

3. It is a noun. (A noun is a person, place, thing, animal, or idea.)

Hint: You can put **c** next to the compound words,
4 next to the words with 4 vowels, and
n next to the nouns.

● Find the **mystery word** below.

without	treehouse	miles per hour
pronounce	greenhouse	flounder
fountain	doghouse	announce
allowed	lost and found	surround
cloudy	brown trout	grouchy
crowded	girl scout	powder

● Read the meaning and the number of letters. Then find the word with that meaning and number of letters hidden in the big word on the right. Put a line under it.

Meaning	Number of Letters	Hidden Words
Belonging to us.	3	SC<u>OUR</u>
Part of a pound.	5	POUNCED
A night bird.	3	GROWLING
Shaped like a ball.	5	BACKGROUND
In what way.	3	SHOWER
Not in.	3	SOUTHERN
Noisy.	4	CLOUDY
Word for person, place, thing, animal, idea.	4	ANNOUNCE
What you say when you get hurt.	4	GROUCHY
Animal that gives milk.	3	SCOWLS
Not on top of.	5	FLOUNDER
The whole amount; not just some.	3	ALLOWANCE
Use oars.	3	EYEBROW

Who made these sounds?

"Bow-wow!"	"No! Not now!"
"Circus time!"	⟨"Meow, meow!"⟩
"Pow-wow!"	"Foul ball!"
"Hoot, hoot!"	"Louder, louder!"
"Squeak, squeak!"	"Wow! Look at that!"
"Moo, moo!"	"Ouch!"

● Fill in the blanks with the words from the top box.

1. The hungry kitten called out, _"Meow, meow!"_

2. As the moon rose, the owl screeched, _____

3. _____, said Laura when she saw the rainbow.

4. The umpire shouted, _____

5. The bouncy puppy yapped, _____

6. The cow called to her calf, _____

7. Mom, in a grouchy mood, told us, _____ with a frown.

8. _____, squealed the mouse when he spied the cat.

9. _____, the clown announced to the audience.

10. The Boy Scout yelled, _____, after he fell down.

Here is another **trick** for reading longer words. You know that if a long word has **one middle consonant**, you try dividing **before the consonant**.

But sometimes you have to divide **after** the consonant because the first vowel is short:

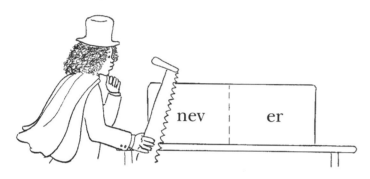

● Put **v c** under the **first vowel** and **middle consonant** in each word. Then draw a line **after** the middle consonant to divide the word into syllables.

nev|er vc	model	second	panel
figure	product	seven	desert
water	solid	liver	rapid
habit	cabin	finish	shadow
level	robin	salad	chisel
	widow	limit	

PLURALS

We usually add **s** or **es** to show more than one (plural). But not all plurals go by the rules. Here are some that don't:

ONE	MORE THAN ONE	ONE	MORE THAN ONE
goose	geese	mouse	mice
tooth	teeth	child	children
foot	feet		

And some words don't change at all to show plural:

ONE	MORE THAN ONE
sheep	sheep
deer	deer
moose	moose

● Fill in the blanks:

SINGULAR (ONE)	PLURAL (MORE THAN ONE)
	feet
goose	
moose	
	children
mouse	
	deer
	sheep
tooth	

● Pick three plurals from the box and write each in a sentence.

_____

_____

_____

_____

_____

Here are some more vowels making a new sound together.

eu
feud

ew
ewe

ew
dew

ew
chew

• Pick the best word to complete each sentence. Write it in the blank.

1. The green sprouts _____ into a large plant.
   (drew, grew, brew)

2. The robin _____ to her nest in the tree.
   (few, feud, flew)

3. Lewis put more oysters into the _____.
   (stew, newt, slew)

4. From the top of the tower, the ranger had a good _____ of the forest.
   (yew, view, vow)

5. A sudden gust of wind _____ my hat off.
   (bloom, brow, blew)

6. The ball game lasted a _____ hours.
   (ewe, few, feud)

7. My aunt _____ how to draw dinosaurs.
   (knew, hew, mew)

8. The princess _____ the jewel into the pond.
   (shrew, threw, chew)

9. Mr. Hewett helped us _____ for the test.
   (review, outgrew, withdrew)

10. At dawn, the ground was wet frow the _____.
    (pew, allow, dew)

● To solve the riddles, fill in the blanks next to the clues. Then write the letters in the numbered boxes.

CLUES A

Made a picture   <u>**D**</u>   <u>   </u>   <u>   </u>   <u>   </u>
                                 11   7   5   2

Also; overly   <u>   </u>   <u>   </u>   <u>   </u>
                                 1   9   3

Has an egg; puts down   <u>   </u>   <u>   </u>   <u>   </u>   <u>   </u>
                                 10   6   4   8

RIDDLE A   What is a fawn after it is one year old?

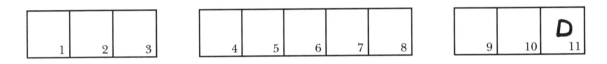

CLUES B

Belonging to us   <u>   </u>   <u>   </u>   <u>   </u>
                                 5   12   1

One of things you chew with   <u>   </u>   <u>   </u>   <u>   </u>   <u>   </u>   <u>   </u>
                                 13   11   3   7   8

Not on   <u>   </u>   <u>   </u>   <u>   </u>
                                 2   6   4

Turned-up bottom of skirt, pants   <u>   </u>   <u>   </u>   <u>   </u>
                                 14   9   10

RIDDLE B   What roof never keeps out the wet?

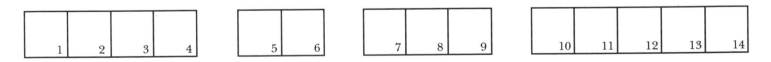

● Help the children finish the school newpaper. Write the best headlines from the lists on the next page.

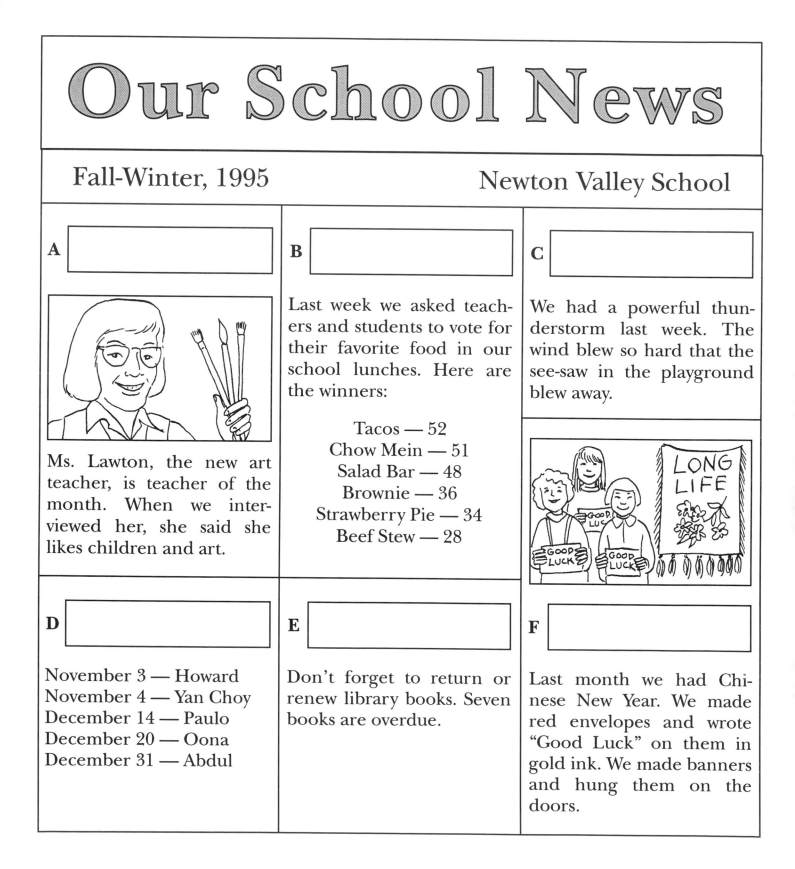

Our School News

Fall-Winter, 1995   Newton Valley School

A

Ms. Lawton, the new art teacher, is teacher of the month. When we interviewed her, she said she likes children and art.

B

Last week we asked teachers and students to vote for their favorite food in our school lunches. Here are the winners:

Tacos — 52
Chow Mein — 51
Salad Bar — 48
Brownie — 36
Strawberry Pie — 34
Beef Stew — 28

C

We had a powerful thunderstorm last week. The wind blew so hard that the see-saw in the playground blew away.

D

November 3 — Howard
November 4 — Yan Choy
December 14 — Paulo
December 20 — Oona
December 31 — Abdul

E

Don't forget to return or renew library books. Seven books are overdue.

F

Last month we had Chinese New Year. We made red envelopes and wrote "Good Luck" on them in gold ink. We made banners and hung them on the doors.

● Circle the best headlines for the newspaper on page 82. Write them in small letters to fit.

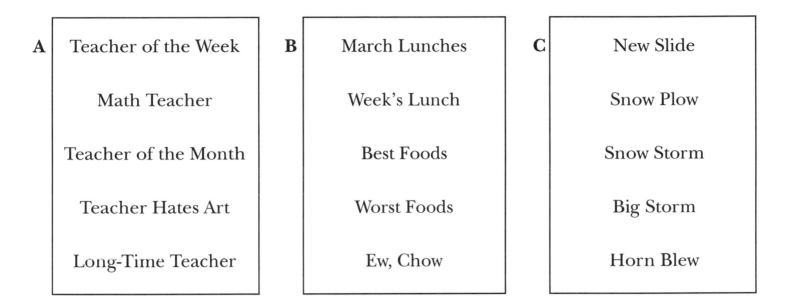

A
Teacher of the Week

Math Teacher

Teacher of the Month

Teacher Hates Art

Long-Time Teacher

B
March Lunches

Week's Lunch

Best Foods

Worst Foods

Ew, Chow

C
New Slide

Snow Plow

Snow Storm

Big Storm

Horn Blew

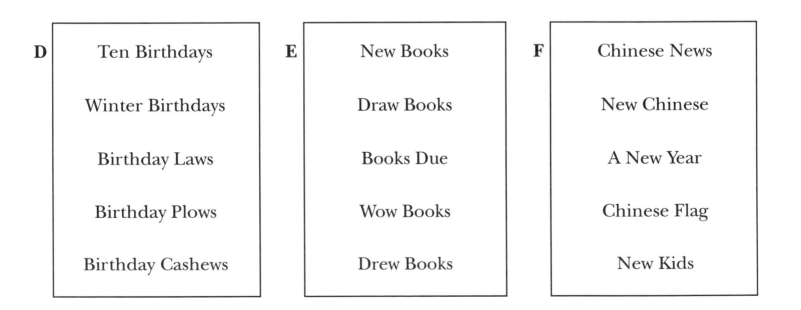

D
Ten Birthdays

Winter Birthdays

Birthday Laws

Birthday Plows

Birthday Cashews

E
New Books

Draw Books

Books Due

Wow Books

Drew Books

F
Chinese News

New Chinese

A New Year

Chinese Flag

New Kids

● Marco's cat ripped the pages out of his journal notebook. Help him put the pages back in order by numbering them **1**, **2**, **3**, and **4**.

Flower is ~~white~~ ~~there~~ the name we gave the kitten we got yesterday.

She is really cute but she has sharp claws. She scratches me when she crawls up my pants leg.

☐

I threw a ball to Flower today, and she fetched it. She purrs a lot.

Flower grew so much in three months! She chows down her cat food. It's my job to feed her.

☐

March 8
We got a new kitten today. She's seven weeks old. We got her from the pet store at the mall.

We haven't picked a name for her. We're thinking of Browny, Paws, Jewel, or Flower.

☐

Flower is getting bigger. She is 2 months old now. She keeps her claws in more than she used to.

We took her to the vet today, and she got a shot. She howled! It was awful.

☐

Here is another **trick** for reading longer words. When you see **le** at the end of a two-syllable word, count back 3 letters from the end of the word to make a syllable.

Give the **le** syllable 3 letters. Divide in front of these 3 letters.

MAGIC SHOW

Then read each syllable as a little word.

help

lit | tle

little = lit + tle

table = ta + ble

● Give the final **le** syllable 3 letters. Divide in front of these 3 letters. Read the words.

little	fiddle	jungle	bugle
table	buckle	title	scribble
bubble	stable	cattle	wiggle
maple	beetle	eagle	staple
giggle	candle	cradle	puddle
stumble	noodle	apple	tickle
uncle	chuckle	tattle	simple
pickle	middle	sparkle	freckle

● Circle:

angle	pebble	bungle	jewel
ankle	poodle	bubble	beagle
lanky	pedal	puddle	angle
auction	paddle	paddle	idle
auk	puddle	poodle	eagle
bugle	sadder	handle	cashew
bungle	stable	huddle	candy
bundle	sidle	candle	candle
blew	settle	hassle	cradle
boggle	saddle	handy	cable
fuzzy	pebble	curdle	jiggle
puddle	people	candle	juggle
dazzle	pepper	crabby	jogger
puzzle	pauper	crackle	jungle
nuzzle	powder	cradle	goggle
belted	table	boggle	sample
leader	title	eagle	stable
bleeder	battle	beagle	steeple
beagle	tattle	beetle	staple
beetle	ladle	bangle	saddle
puddle	throttle	pablum	brittle
babble	bottle	puddles	riddle
bugle	bother	pestle	bridle
rubble	bustle	pebbles	ripple
bubble	beetle	paddles	brides

● Put the words in the box in pairs below. A sample is done for you.

riddle	snuggle	bridle	poodle
bugle	(rattle)	wrinkle	ankle
tackle	knuckle	cuddle	puzzle
(cradle)	noodle	fumble	dimple
saddle	beagle	fiddle	apple

cradle , _rattle_ (for a baby)

_____ , _____ (food)

_____ , _____ (dogs)

_____ , _____ (body parts)

_____ , _____ (lines on the face)

_____ , _____ (things that make music)

_____ , _____ (ways to hug)

_____ , _____ (football moves)

_____ , _____ (something to solve)

_____ , _____ (something to put on a horse)

Snuggle	Bicycle	Staples	Tables	Goggles	Recycled
Bugles	Noodles	bottles	Saddle	Puzzles	Eagle

● Fill in the blanks with words from the top box.

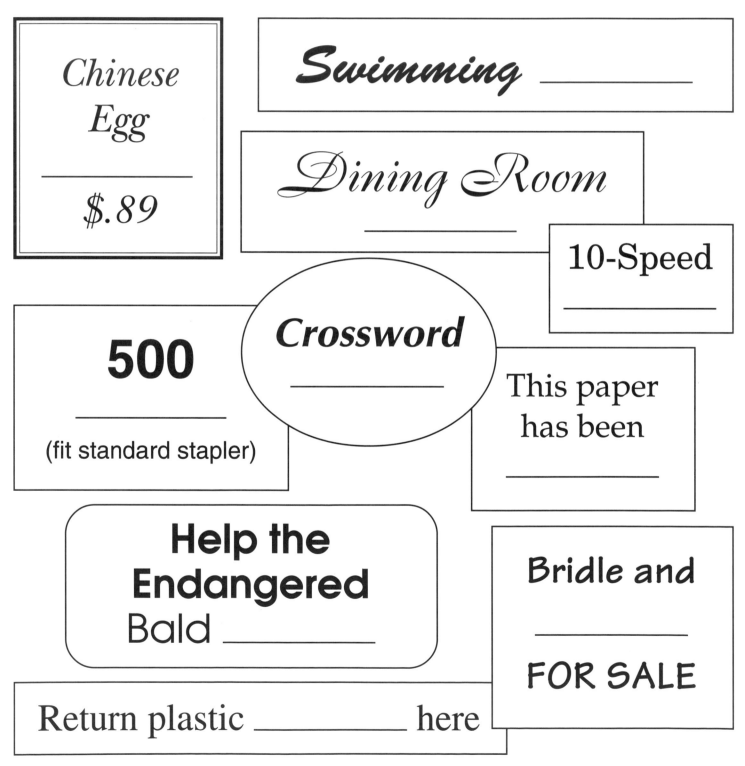

Chinese
Egg
_____
$.89

Swimming _____

Dining Room
_____

10-Speed
_____

500
_____
(fit standard stapler)

Crossword
_____

This paper
has been
_____

**Help the
Endangered**
Bald _____

Bridle and
_____
FOR SALE

Return plastic _____ here

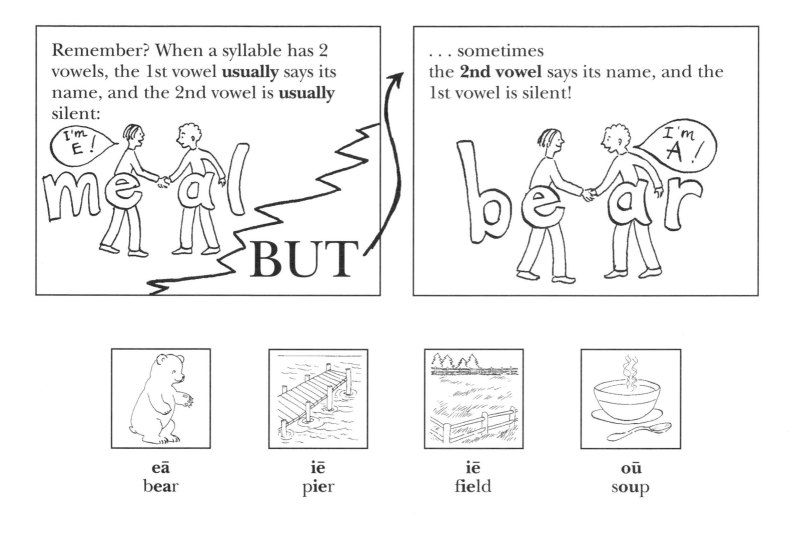

Remember? When a syllable has 2 vowels, the 1st vowel **usually** says its name, and the 2nd vowel is **usually** silent:

I'm E!

me a l

BUT

. . . sometimes the **2nd vowel** says its name, and the 1st vowel is silent!

I'm A!

be a r

eā
bear

iē
pier

iē
field

oū
soup

● Pick the best word to complete each sentence. Write it in the blank.

1. The frisky pony galloped across the _____.
   (field, brief, feel)

2. Dad sipped the chicken noodle _____ that he made.
   (group, route, soup)

3. "_____ are so cute!" said Lou, cuddling the kitten.
   (Shriek, You, Youth)

4. Aunt Lizzie and Uncle Ted wrapped a birthday gift for their _____.
   (wear, niece, belief)

5. "It's too hot to _____ my coat!" said Asha.
   (tear, bear, wear)

wear	caribou	cookie	steak
great aunt	field	thief	pear
cougar	piece	prairie	break
pier	Freddie	prairie dog	niece
soup	polar bear	pig pen	shriek

● Fill in the blanks with words from the top box.

ANIMALS

1. _____

2. _____

3. _____

4. _____

FOODS

1. _____

2. _____

3. _____

4. _____

PEOPLE

1. _____

2. _____

3. _____

4. _____

PLACES

1. _____

2. _____

3. _____

4. _____

BEAR   Cashier   Chief   Soup   Cookie   Diesel

Break   Route   GREAT   Pears   FIELD   Fairy

● Fill in the blanks with words from the top box.

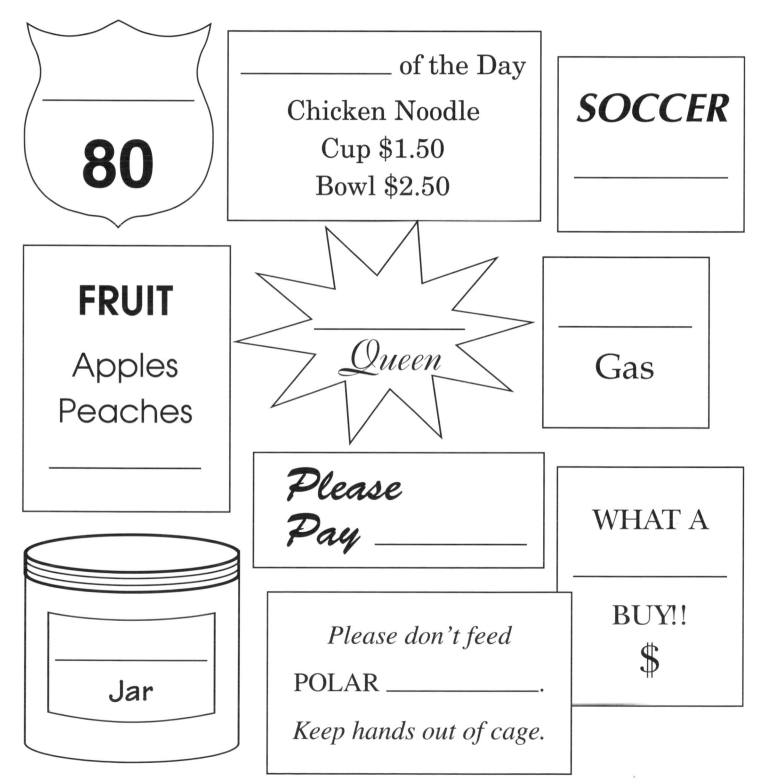

• Pick words from the box to match the definitions. Then find and circle these words on the grid. After you have found all the words, write the leftover letters in the spaces at the bottom to solve the riddles.

wears	pier	your	soup
(pear)	chief	route	group
tears	shield	great	piece
bear	fields	four	niece

A kind of fruit   **p e a r**

Meadows   _ _ _ _ _ _

A food like stew   _ _ _ _

Super   _ _ _ _ _

Has clothes on   _ _ _ _ _

Belonging to you   _ _ _ _

Nephew or   _ _ _ _ _

Rips   _ _ _ _ _

A set of people or things   _ _ _ _ _

A ____ of paper   _ _ _ _ _

Polar ____   _ _ _ _

Piece of armor   _ _ _ _ _ _

Landing place   _ _ _ _

W	P	E	A	R	W	E	A	R	S
H	I	E	N	T	H	E	Y	A	O
B	E	A	R	R	E	G	B	A	U
R	C	E	P	I	E	R	-	G	P
Y	E	F	O	O	T	E	A	R	S
O	T	E	D	W	H	A	E	O	N
U	I	T	I	S	M	T	A	U	D
R	F	I	E	L	D	S	E	P	I
N	T	O	S	H	I	E	L	D	A
N	I	E	C	E	R	U	L	E	R

When are boys like bears?

_ _ _ _ _ _ _ _ _ _ _ _ _ _ _ _ _ - _ _ _ _ _ _

When is a piece of wood like a queen?

_ _ _ _ _ _ _ _ _ _ _ _ _ _ _ _ _ _ _ _ _ _

92

Now you know that when a syllable has 2 vowels together,

- the first vowel **usually** says its name; but
- sometimes the second vowel says its name.

Here's some news:

- Sometimes the first vowel makes the short sound, or a similar sound.

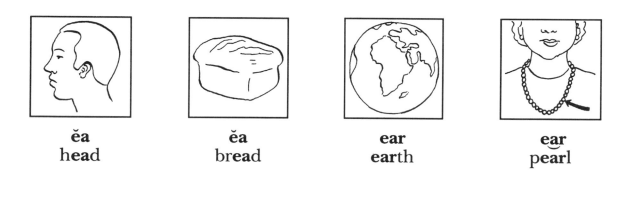

ĕa
head

ĕa
bread

ear
earth

ear
pearl

● Write:

learn	heavy	meadow	sweat	earth
search	head	sweater	earn	feather

<table>
<tr><td>_____</td><td>_____</td><td>_____</td><td>_____</td></tr>
<tr><td>_____</td><td>_____</td><td>_____</td><td>_____</td></tr>
</table>

93

● Where do the words in the box belong?

earth	earthworm	jewelry box
field	bread box	pearl earrings
early	heather	gingerbread mix
instead	bedspread	ready to learn
meadow	mountain	leather chair

INSIDE

1. _____
2. _____
3. _____
4. _____
5. _____
6. _____

OUTSIDE

1. _____
2. _____
3. _____
4. _____
5. _____
6. _____

● Fill in the blanks with words from the top box.

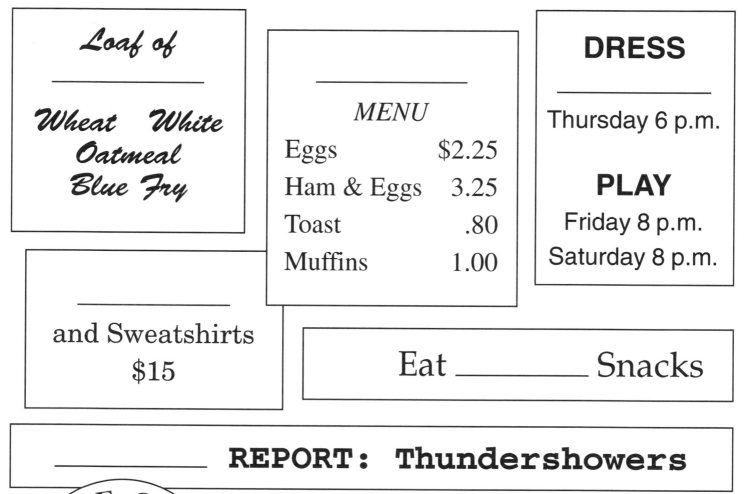

Loaf of

_____

Wheat   White
Oatmeal
Blue   Fry

MENU

_____

Eggs	$2.25
Ham & Eggs	3.25
Toast	.80
Muffins	1.00

DRESS

_____

Thursday 6 p.m.

PLAY

Friday 8 p.m.
Saturday 8 p.m.

_____

and Sweatshirts
$15

Eat _____ Snacks

_____ REPORT: Thundershowers

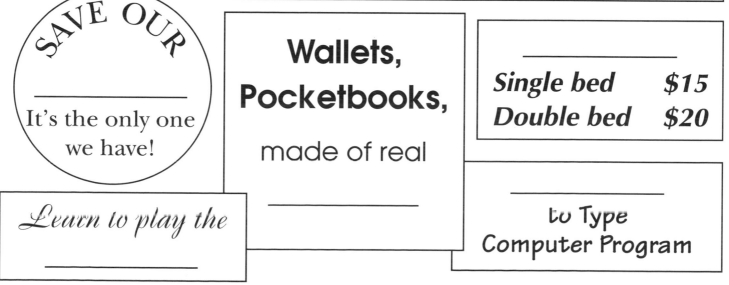

SAVE OUR

_____

It's the only one
we have!

Wallets,
Pocketbooks,

made of real

_____

Single bed $15
Double bed $20

Learn to play the

_____

_____ to Type
Computer Program

● Write **true** or **false** after each sentence.

A feather is heavy.

You can eat a piece of bread.

A meadow is like a field.

A polar bear likes hot weather.

A sweater is a thing you can wear.

A cougar is a fierce cat.

We eat cookie soup for breakfast.

A pear is a kind of meat.

If I run far I will be out of breath.

You can eat a piece of leather.

Being early is the same as being late.

An earthworm is made of lead.

Eating fruit helps you to be healthy.

Here are some other surprising letter groups:

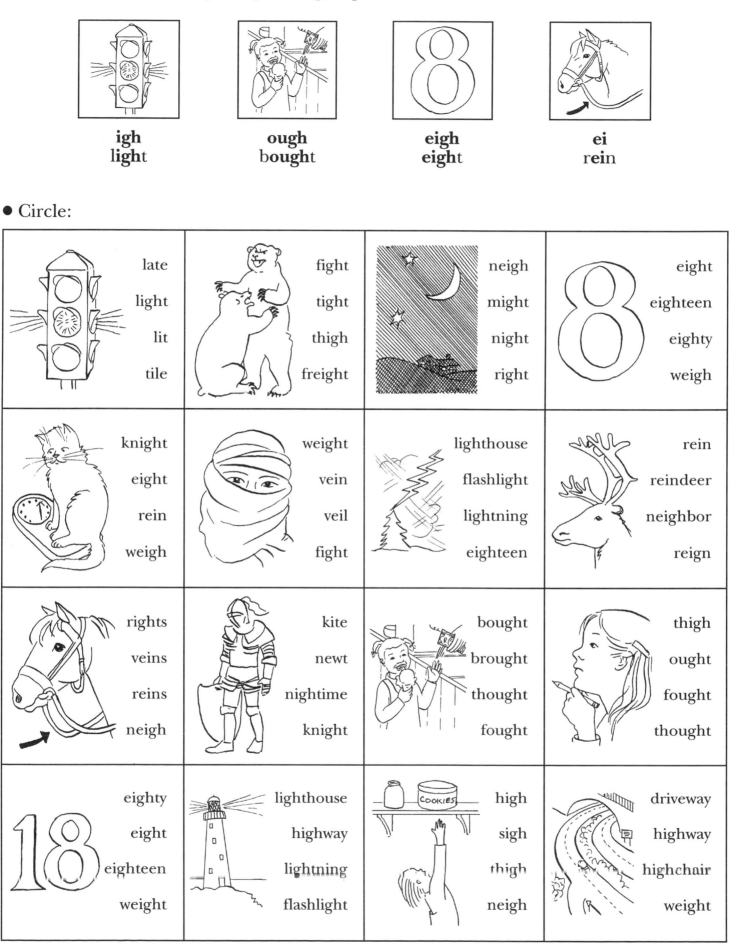

igh
light

ough
bough**t**

eigh
eight

ei
rei**n**

● Circle:

late / **light** / lit / tile	fight / tight / thigh / freight	neigh / might / **night** / right	**eight** / eighteen / eighty / weigh
knight / eight / rein / weigh	weight / vein / **veil** / fight	lighthouse / flashlight / **lightning** / eighteen	rein / **reindeer** / neighbor / reign
rights / veins / **reins** / neigh	kite / newt / nightime / **knight**	bought / **brought** / thought / fought	thigh / ought / fought / **thought**
eighty / eight / **eighteen** / weight	**lighthouse** / highway / lightning / flashlight	high / sigh / **thigh** / neigh	driveway / **highway** / highchair / weight

● Cross out the word on each pad that does not belong:

Pad 1:
eight
eighteen
tight
sixteen
eighty-five

Pad 2:
bought
light
brought
fought
caught

Pad 3:
reindeer
bear
cougar
flashlight
caribou

Pad 4:
lightning
thunder
rain
wind
skein

Pad 5:
heard
sleigh
sled
ice skates
skidoo

Pad 6:
sun
lamp
believe
flashlight
candle

Pad 7:
niece
nephew
break
aunt
uncle

Pad 8:
field
chief
meadow
lawn
valley

Pad 9:
thigh
knee
hip
spread
ankle

● Fill in the blanks with words from the top box.

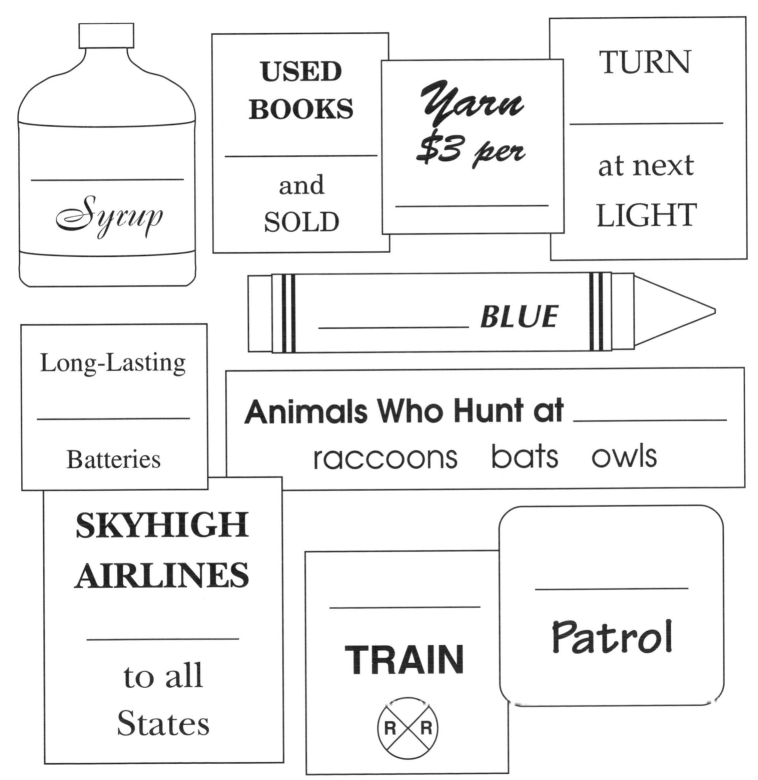

Words that sound the same but are spelled differently are called **homonyms**.

Examples: to — too
cent — sent
hear — here

● For each word in Column A there is a homonym in Column B. Write the number of its homonym next to each word in Column A.

A		B
wait	_____	1. sighed
ceiling	_____	2. whether
piece	_____	3. weight
side	_____	4. choose
threw	_____	5. sealing
vain	_____	6. eight
weather	_____	7. peace
no	_____	8. heard
chews	_____	9. break
brake	_____	10. pear
ate	_____	11. through
herd	_____	12. know
hire	_____	13. vein
pair	_____	14. higher
bare	_____	15. bear

Watch out! These are trick questions!

● Here are some problems to solve.
Think carefully.

My neighbor has eight sleighs.

Each sleigh is pulled by eight reindeer.

Each reindeer weighs eighty pounds.

Each sleigh weighs eighteen pounds.

If eight reindeer are pulling eight sleighs, how much freight do the sleighs carry altogether?

_____ Why? _____

_____

One night, the knight had a frightful nightmare. He dreamed that the high tower of the castle was struck by lightning. The tower caught on fire, and the fire was so bright that it was like daylight.

The king, queen, prince, princess, and eighteen pages were too frightened to move. The mighty knight had to save them.

How many people did the knight save? _____

Why? _____

[Zero. It was all a dream.] [Zero. The sleighs aren't carrying anything.]

olt
colt

old
cold

ild
ch**ild**

ind
kind

● Pick the best word to complete each sentence. Write it in the blank.

1. "You are very _____ to help me," said the

   old man to the child.

scold
colt
kind
cold

2. Hundreds of _____ horses roam the plains

   in the Western United States.

mild
wild
wind
most

3. Because Ms. Holt is _____, she has a seeing-

   eye dog to help her.

blind
bind
bold
brief

4. You can make a hat by _____ a piece of

   paper.

scolding
folding
minding
find

5. Ebo _____ about his new neighbor during

   Sharing Time.

mold
bolt
hold
told

6. By the time we reached the store, all the comic books

   had been _____.

scold
bind
breath
sold

healthy	toll	high chair	wild cat
scold	wild	hostess	both
hold	cold	colt	fold
neighbor	weigh	find	cougar
prairie dog	reindeer	old	niece
heaven	host	gold	grind
brown bear	kind	child	guy

● Fill in the blanks with words from the top box.

PEOPLE

1. _____
2. _____
3. _____
4. _____
5. _____
6. _____

ANIMALS

1. _____
2. _____
3. _____
4. _____
5. _____
6. _____

VERBS (doing words)

1. _____
2. _____
3. _____
4. _____
5. _____
6. _____

ADJECTIVES (describing words)

1. _____
2. _____
3. _____
4. _____
5. _____
6. _____

Bolt	FIND	SOLD	cold	Rolls	WILD
Colt	Post	Gold	Patrol	Trolls	Child

● Fill in the blanks with words from the top box.

_____-A-WORD PUZZLES

HOUSE SALE

Earrings
_____
and Silver

_____
for sale
2 years old,
bay gelding,
likes people

U.S.
_____ Office

State Police
Speed _____

_____
WEST RODEO

Fresh-baked
_____
with butter
$.80

Cinema Movies
Adult $5.00
_____ $3.00

Today's Weather:
_____ with
a high of 30°

● Use these words to solve the crossword puzzle:

tag	end	ear	field	piece	~~freight~~
tin	or	eat	fight	reign	thought
yes	hot	told	tight	coughs	sweaters
to	red	fold	group	eighty	weather
		toe	wild		

ACROSS

1. Cargo, baggage.
5. End part of the foot.
6. Opposite of tame.
7. What she does when she is sick.
9. To finish, stop.
11. Toward.
12. Part of something, such as a cake.
14. Opposite of loose.
15. Argue.
16. To rule, as a king or queen would.
18. To gobble up.
19. Opposite of no.
20. Will he __ won't he?
21. Did tell.

DOWN

1. Crease, bend something over.
2. Color of most apples.
3. Set of people or things.
4. Game of chasing.
5. Silver metal some cans are made from.
6. It can be sunny, cloudy, or stormy.
8. Knitted clothes.
10. Opposite of cold.
11. Did think.
13. Eight times ten.
15. Meadow.
17. What we hear with.

PROVERBS

Proverbs are sayings that tell you something about life. Different proverbs can have the same meanings.

The proverbs in the squares mean the same as the proverbs in the hexagons. Draw a line from each proverb to the circle containing its meaning.

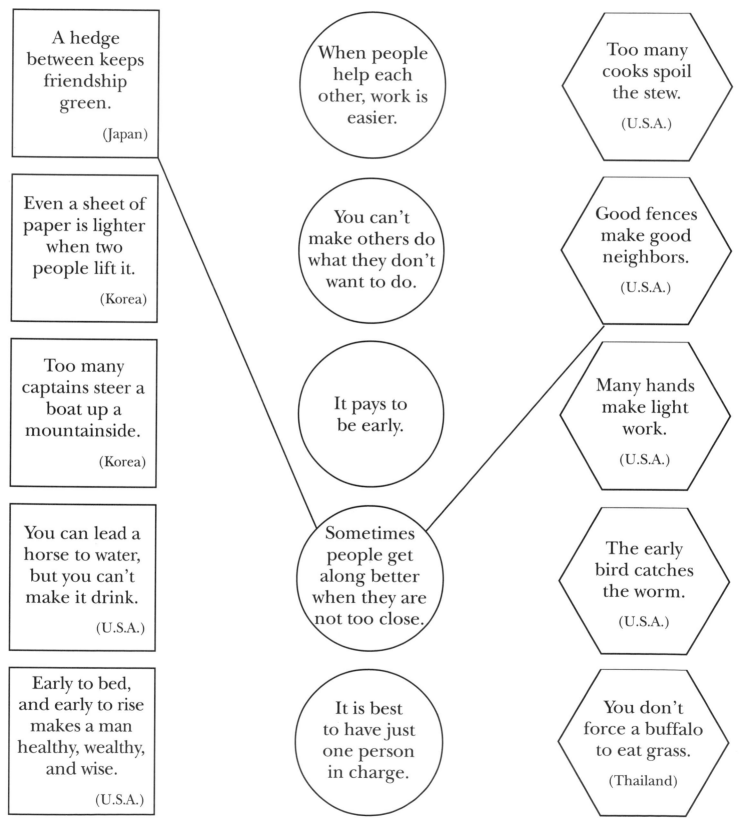

A hedge between keeps friendship green.

(Japan)

Even a sheet of paper is lighter when two people lift it.

(Korea)

Too many captains steer a boat up a mountainside.

(Korea)

You can lead a horse to water, but you can't make it drink.

(U.S.A.)

Early to bed, and early to rise makes a man healthy, wealthy, and wise.

(U.S.A.)

When people help each other, work is easier.

You can't make others do what they don't want to do.

It pays to be early.

Sometimes people get along better when they are not too close.

It is best to have just one person in charge.

Too many cooks spoil the stew.

(U.S.A.)

Good fences make good neighbors.

(U.S.A.)

Many hands make light work.

(U.S.A.)

The early bird catches the worm.

(U.S.A.)

You don't force a buffalo to eat grass.

(Thailand)

PROBLEMS TO SOLVE

1. Yoko is far away from home. The weather is colder than she thought it would be. She only brought shorts and short-sleeved shirts, but no sweater, sweatshirt, or long pants. She only has eighty-eight cents. She has a friend who lives nearby, but she can't remember her address.

   ● Help her solve her problem. What can she do? _____

   _____

   _____

   _____

   _____

2. The children in the neighborhood want to build a treehouse. They think they can find a tree to use. They collected a few old boards from neighbors, but they need more lumber. They have eighteen cents between them.

   ● Help them solve their problem. What can they do? _____

   _____

   _____

   _____

107

MAGIC TRICKS

● Try these tricks on your friends:

1.   *Ahead of time:* Hide four pennies in the back binding of a book.

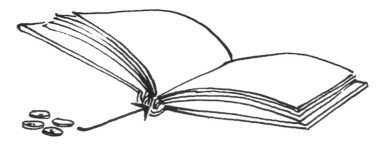

Tell the audience you are going to hide four pennies in a book, and that you will double the number of coins in the book. Let the audience see you place the pennies on a page. Close the book. Say some magic words. When you open it, pour all eight pennies into their hands.

2.   *Ahead of time:* Hide a toothpick inside the hem of a piece of cloth.

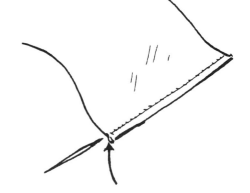

Let the audience see you put a whole toothpick in the middle of the cloth. Tell them you will wrap up the toothpick and then break it. Let them see you do it and hear the "SNAP!" (*But you will be breaking the toothpick in the hem.*) Then unwrap the cloth and show the toothpick still whole!

The letters **ture** and **sure** sound like /cher/ and /zher/:

pic**ture**   furni**ture**   mea**sure**

● Use the words in the box to complete the sentences below:

adventure	fracture	temperature
punctured	picture	stature
nature	mixture	furniture
future	measure	pasture

We cannot know what will happen in the _____.

The X-ray showed a _____ in Zeb's left arm.

When Matsu was sick, her _____ was high.

The horses grazed in the green _____.

Paz added flour to the cookie batter and stirred the _____.

Joe took a _____ of his dog with his new camera.

All living things and the earth are part of _____.

Dad told the kids that they were going on an _____.

Mom moved around the _____ in the house.

The nail _____ the tire on Eileen's bike.

Picture	pleasure	Pastures	Temperature
Future	TREASURE	Punctures	adventure
Lecture	Nature	FURNITURE	Measuring

● Fill in the blanks with words from the top box.

Go on an _____

The Car of the _____ !!
Solar-powered

Hike on the _____ *Trail*

_____
HUNT
1:00 p.m.

_____
SALE TODAY
tables   chairs
sofas   beds

_____
Cups
pint
quart
gallon

_____
Frames

It's been a _____
to serve you.

_____
High 80°   Low 52°

Fix Tire _____
Here

● Circle the letter that marks the treasure.

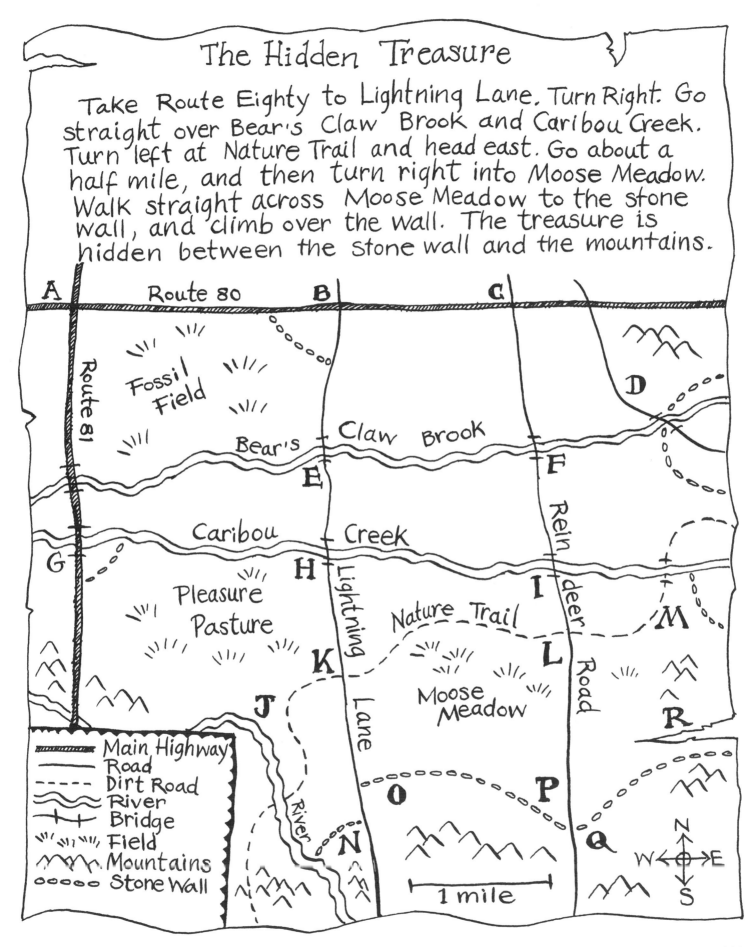

The Hidden Treasure

Take Route Eighty to Lightning Lane. Turn Right. Go straight over Bear's Claw Brook and Caribou Creek. Turn left at Nature Trail and head east. Go about a half mile, and then turn right into Moose Meadow. Walk straight across Moose Meadow to the stone wall, and climb over the wall. The treasure is hidden between the stone wall and the mountains.

SOLVE the RIDDLES

● Try to solve the riddles yourself or find the answers in the mixed-up list below. Write the letter on the line.

1. What is the highest pleasure you can think of? _____

2. What did the big firecracker say to the little firecracker? _____

   _____

3. Which is heavier, a pound of feathers or a pound of bricks? _____

4. What is the highest building in a town or city? _____

5. When is it right to lie? _____

6. What changes a pear to a pearl? _____

7. What ant is the youngest? _____

8. What goes up but never comes down? _____

9. When is a piece of wood like a queen? _____

10. What has eighteen legs and catches flies? _____

a. The letter L.

b. Riding in an airplane.

c. A baseball team.

d. The library, because it has the most stories.

e. When it is made into a ruler.

f. Neither. Both weigh one pound.

g. An infant.

h. Your age.

i. My pop's bigger than your pop.

j. When you are sleeping in bed.

MEASURING

● Fill in the blanks.

If you measured a feather, it would be about as long as a _____.

(walrus, pencil, pasture)

If you measured a football field, it would be about as wide as a _____.

(parking lot, sweater, reindeer)

A flashlight weighs about as much as a _____.

(candle, cougar, niece)

If you measured a high chair, it would be about as tall as a _____.

(polar bear, gold ring, child)

The temperature of an ice cube is about the same as the temperature of

_____.

(lightning, a snow flake, hot soup)

A glass of milk could fill up a _____.

(trash can, freight train, measuring cup)

A sweater weighs about as much as a _____.

(picture frame, wild cat, neighbor)

If you measured a loaf of bread, it would be about as long as _____.

(the earth, a jewelry box, a mountain)

Sounds can be clues to meaning but so can **word parts**.

You already learned that ⌐er⌐ can be added to a word to mean **a person who**.

⌐or⌐ can do the same thing.

● Write:

farm ⌐	⌐er	_farmer_	a person who _farms_
help ⌐	⌐er	_____	a person who _____
act ⌐	⌐or	_____	a person who _____
direct ⌐	⌐or	_____	a person who _____
visit ⌐	⌐or	_____	a person who _____
edit ⌐	⌐or	_____	a person who _____
invent ⌐	⌐or	_____	a person who _____
conduct ⌐	⌐or	_____	a person who _____
collect ⌐	⌐or	_____	a person who _____

An ending that can be added to a word to change its meaning is called a ⌐**suffix** .

⌐Word   +   ⌐suffix   =   New ⌐ Word

If you start with a doing word, or	and	add	you get	a person
VERB⌐	+	⌐er or	=	NOUN

114

Proverbs are wise sayings that say something about life. What do you think these proverbs mean?

• Below each proverb, tell what you think it means.

1. The reason for doing it right today is tomorrow.

   Doing a job well now can save you problems later.

2. An apple a day keeps the doctor away.

3. A friend in need is a friend indeed.

4. The pen is mightier than the sword.

5. Two wrongs don't make a right.

6. Work like a dog, and eat like a king.

7. Don't start up a tree you cannot climb.

8. Sitcks and stones can break my bones, but words can never hurt me.

Here's the **Doubling** Rule.

Sometimes the spelling of a word is changed **before a suffix is added**.

If a suffix beginning with a vowel is added to a **CVC** word, the final consonant in the **CVC** word is doubled to keep the first vowel short.

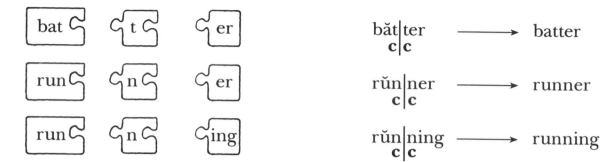

bắt|ter $\longrightarrow$ batter
c|c

rŭn|ner $\longrightarrow$ runner
c|c

rŭn|ning $\longrightarrow$ running
c|c

● Double the final consonant of the **CVC** word before adding an ending that begins with a vowel.

sit + er _____	spin + er _____	
jog + er _____	spin + ing _____	
win + er _____	bag + er _____	
win + ing _____	sit + ing _____	
stop + er _____	snap + er _____	

● Pick the best word to complete each sentence. Write it in the blank.

1. At the supermarket, the _____ packed the food in brown paper bags.
   (bagged, bagger, bagging)

2. The traffic light turned yellow, and the cars _____ on the white line.
   (stopped, stopper, stopping)

3. The score was tied, 3 to 3. The crowd cheered as the _____ hit the ball over the fence.
   (batted, batter, bater)

The Doubling Rule only applies to **CVC** words that have a **short vowel** and **end in one consonant** when the ending begins with a vowel:

băt ter ⟶ batter
c   c

CVCC words do not need doubling:

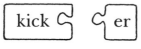

kĭc ker ⟶ kicker
c   c

Words with other vowel sounds do not need doubling:

wāi ter ⟶ waiter
vv   c

No doubling is needed when the ending begins with a consonant.

bĭg ness ⟶ bigness
c   c

● Add the endings, doubling when needed.

kick	+	er	_____	jump	+	er	_____
zip	+	er	_____	tell	+	er	_____
let	+	er	_____	meet	+	ing	_____
camp	+	er	_____	get	+	ing	_____
heat	+	ed	_____	buzz	+	er	_____
rain	+	ing	_____	disk	+	s	_____
land	+	ing	_____	ask	+	ing	_____
band	+	s	_____	golf	+	er	_____

Here's the **Silent-e** Rule. You know that sometimes a letter is **doubled** before adding an ending. Sometimes a letter is **dropped** before adding an ending.

> If a suffix beginning with a vowel is added to a **silent-e** (**VCe**) word, the **silent-e** is dropped.

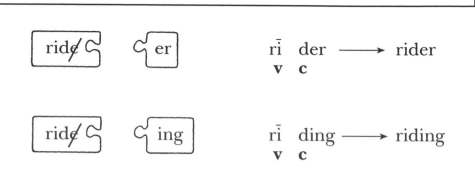

● Add endings:

ride	+	er	_____
make	+	ing	_____
hike	+	er	_____
hike	+	ing	_____
hike	+	ed	_____
doze	+	ed	_____
doze	+	ing	_____
vote	+	er	_____
vote	+	ing	_____

vote	+	ed	_____
dine	+	er	_____
dine	+	ing	_____
bake	+	er	_____
bake	+	ing	_____
bake	+	ed	_____
care	+	ing	_____
shine	+	ing	_____
blame	+	ed	_____

118

● Cross out the word on each pad that does not belong:

Pad 1:
doctor
inventor
visitor
jumped
teacher

Pad 2:
author
farmer
bigger
mayor
actor

Pad 3:
longer
wider
higher
helping
shorter

Pad 4:
editor
floor
writer
director
author

Pad 5:
madder
sadder
happier
sillier
teacher

Pad 6:
collector
conductor
advisor
back door
professor

Pad 7:
furniture
nature
armchair
table
rocking chair

Pad 8:
brighter
darker
lighter
baker
dimmer

Pad 9:
hiker
biker
smaller
walker
runner

You learned that verbs can be changed to nouns by adding **er**.

Verbs can also be changed to nouns by adding the suffixes **tion** ("shun") and **sion** ("zhun").

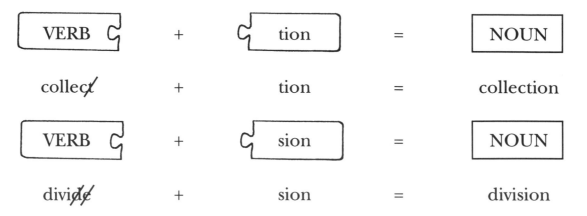

| VERB | + | tion | = | NOUN |

collec~~t~~ + tion = collection

| VERB | + | sion | = | NOUN |

divi~~de~~ + sion = division

● Read the words in the box. Then use the words to finish the sentences below.

fractions	directions	television
lotion	pollution	explosion
caution	station	invention
invitation	addition	vacation

1. Our family had fun on our _____ at the beach.

2. Una added up the numbers on her _____ paper.

3. Neil put _____ on the itchy spot on his hand.

4. The train stopped at the next _____.

5. Thomas Edison's most famous _____ is the light bulb.

6. One-half (½) and two-thirds (⅔) are _____.

7. We made a paper airplane by reading the _____ in a book.

8. Dirt in the air, water, or earth is called _____.

9. Jasmin's friend sent her an _____ to the party.

10. Some people believe it is harmful to watch too much _____.

120

● Match the teacher comments to the description of the student's work by writing the number of the comment in the blank.

① Great subtraction!

② You have my permission.

③ Nice Co-operation!

④ What an invention!

⑫ Super addition! ☺

⑤ Thanks for the invitation!

⑪ Good job on fractions!

⑥ 100% right!!

⑩ Sounds like a fun vacation!

⑦ I understand your confusion. Please see me.

⑨ You followed directions well.

⑧ What a pleasure to read your story!

_____ Heidi wrote a composition about her vacation.

_____ Earl and the children in his group worked together to make a poster.

_____ Eileen asked if she could bring her cousin to school tomorrow.

_____ Hanee matched fractions to illustrations.

_____ Dakota got every problem correct on her math paper.

_____ Hoang invited Mr. Lopez to his flute recital.

_____ Cai did well on a page of "take-aways."

_____ Pearl invented a battery-powered robot.

_____ Janet wrote a story about a stray cat finding a home.

_____ Dwight made an origami bird by listening to directions.

_____ Lou wrote a note to the teacher, telling her he was confused.

_____ Nina added a page of numbers.

Kayley is going to give a report about birds to her class.

● Read this article on birds from the encyclopedia. Then help her take notes on the information (See next page).

BIRDS

There are many kinds of birds with different ways of life, but all birds have feathers, two legs, and a beak. All birds have wings, but not all birds can fly. Birds have hollow bones, which make them lighter for flying. Air in the hollow bones also provides built-in air-conditioning. It keeps them cool.

Homes

Birds live all over the world, in hot and cold regions, on land and on, or near, the water. Some land birds live near trees or forests. Others prefer open, grassy meadows or fields. Some water birds live near the sea or ocean. Others are fresh-water birds, living by rivers, ponds, or lakes. Some breeds of bird migrate from salt water to fresh water habitats.

Nests

Birds hatch from eggs. Most birds build nests into which they lay their eggs, but some kinds of birds simply find a safe place to lay their eggs. A few breeds lay their eggs in other birds' nests.

Both the male and female adults of some kinds of birds sit on the eggs to keep them warm.

Food

Different kinds of birds eat different things, but birds eat a lot, considering their size and weight. Their food includes seeds, berries, and other fruit, insects, fish, other birds, and small animals.

122

● Now help Kayley finish her outline of the information she learned from the encyclopedia by filling in the shaded boxes.

Title: [   ]

A. What all birds have
   1. [   ] (but don't all fly)
   2. two [   ]
   3. beak
   4. [f   ]
   5. [   ] bones

B. Where birds live
   1. hot or [   ] areas
   2. forests or grassy [   ]
   3. near water

C. Birds' nests
   1. build them
   2. find safe place to [   ]
   3. use other birds' [   ]

D. [   ]
   1. seeds
   2. berries, fruit
   3. insects
   4. [   ]
   5. other birds
   6. small animals

● Use the words in the box to help Kayley finish her report.

fields	steal	feathers	lay
their	bones	father	weather

Birds

by

Birds all have _____ wings, beaks, and two legs. They have _____ that are hollow. This helps them to fly.

Birds live in hot and cold _____. They live in forests, in _____, or near the water.

Most birds _____ their eggs in nests. The mother and _____ birds both hatch the eggs. Some birds _____ nests from other birds instead of building _____ own.

124

Other suffixes that usually change verbs to nouns are **ment**, **ance**, **ence**, and **age** ("idge").

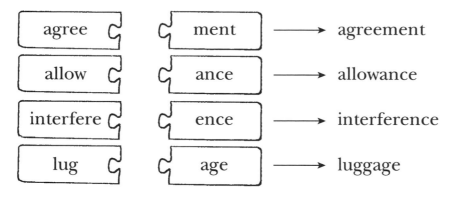

agree + ment → agreement

allow + ance → allowance

interfere + ence → interference

lug + age → luggage

● Fill in the blanks with the words in the boxes.

The _____ truck got _____ from the collision.	damaged garbage
The nurse put a _____ on Eli's cut to keep him from getting an _____.	bandage infection
"Please pay _____ as I give the _____," said the teacher.	directions attention
Abu used his _____ to buy a stamp for his stamp _____.	allowance collection
Mr. Rios forgot to put _____ on the _____ after he wrapped it.	package postage
The _____ waited in _____ for the play to begin.	silence audience
"I want to meet the _____ who created this _____," said Keiko.	inventor invention
Our family took five pieces of _____ when we went on _____.	vacation luggage

Garbage	Ambulance	Voltage	Messages
Postage	Silence	Appointments	LUGGAGE
package	Entrance	Attendance	basement

● Fill in the blanks with words from the top box.

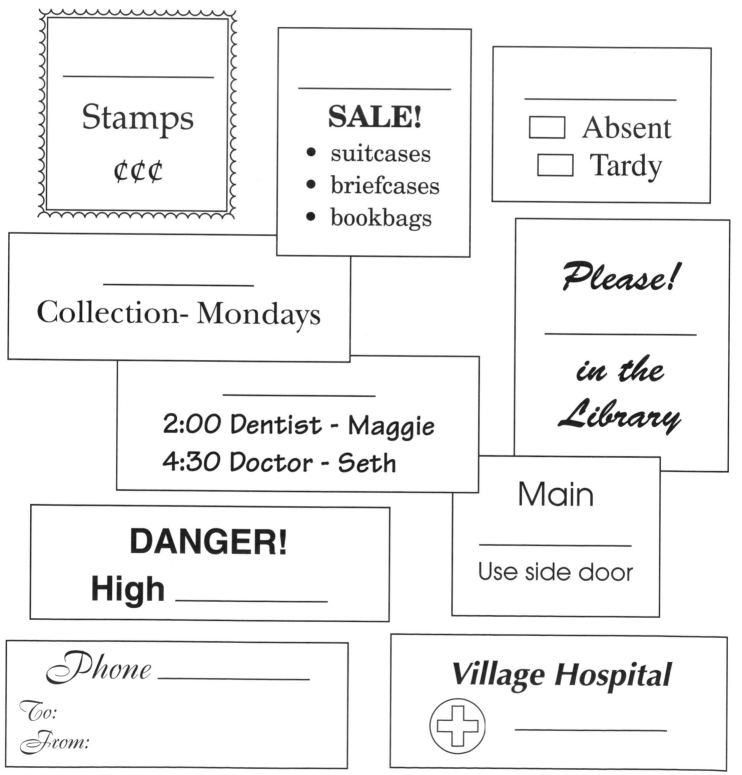

_____
Stamps
¢¢¢

_____
SALE!
- suitcases
- briefcases
- bookbags

_____
☐ Absent
☐ Tardy

_____
Collection- Mondays

_____
2:00 Dentist - Maggie
4:30 Doctor - Seth

Please!
_____
in the
Library

Main
_____
Use side door

DANGER!
High _____

Phone _____
To:
From:

Village Hospital
✚ _____

Some suffixes change **adjectives** to **nouns.**

One example is **-ness**

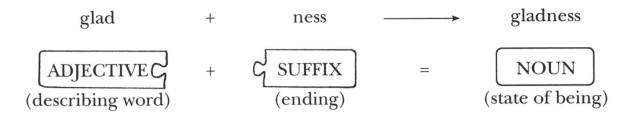

glad   +   ness   ⟶   gladness

ADJECTIVE   +   SUFFIX   =   NOUN

(describing word)   (ending)   (state of being)

● Draw a line between the opposites in Columns 1 and 2.

1	2
sourness	dryness
dampness	lightness
brightness	rudeness
gladness	sweetness
darkness	dimness
politeness	sadness

● Pick a word from column 1 to finish each sentence.

1. Kenya could barely see the shape of her cat in the _____.

2. Felix squinted his eyes because of the _____ of the sun.

3. The _____ of the grass made the dog's fur wet.

4. When she woke up on her birthday, Mitsu was filled with _____.

5. Gene made a funny face when he tasted the _____ of the lemon.

6. "I like your _____," said Grandfather, after Min Yong said, "Please" and "Thank you."

Some suffixes turn words or word parts into **verbs**, or doing words. One example is ᑫ**en** .

black + en $\longrightarrow$ blacken

ADJECTIVE + SUFFIX = VERB
(describing word) (ending) (doing word)

● Use the ᑫ**en** words in the box to complete the sentences below.

| widen | darken | straighten | shorten | fatten |
| liken | flatten | lighten | lengthen | weaken |

You can _____ paint by adding black paint to it.

"Let me _____ your load," said Eugene as he took one of the packages Gran was carrying.

Mom thinks her dress is too long, so she wants to _____ the hem.

Dad used his hand to _____ the balls of cookie batter before he baked them.

The construction workers are going to _____ the road to make a three-lane highway.

Joyce got braces on her teeth to _____ them.

Being sick for a long time may _____ your body.

Mother will _____ her vacation so the family can visit Gran and Gramps longer.

The vet told Roy to _____ up the puppy by giving her more food.

● Help Thema finish writing the pages in her diary by adding **en** or **ness** to the words under the blanks. Then put the pages in order by numbering them in the boxes.

page ☐

This will make dark brown paint. I will use it to paint cornrows on my hair.

page ☐

After the face paint is dry, I will paint my hair. This time I will _____ (dark) the brown paint by adding black.

page ☐

When the puppets are smooth we can paint the faces. I will _____ (light) the brown paint with white to make light brown paint for my skin.

page ☐

When the puppet is all painted I will make the body out of a piece of Kente cloth. This is to honor my African ancestors.

page ☐

We made puppets at camp today. They are self portraits. They are going to _____ (hard) over-night. I hope that the _____ (damp) in the air doesn't keep them from drying.

page ☐

Tomorrow, if the puppets are dry, we will get them ready to paint. We will smooth the sharp edges of clay with sandpaper to get rid of the _____. (rough)

There are also suffixes that turn words into **adjectives**, or describing words.

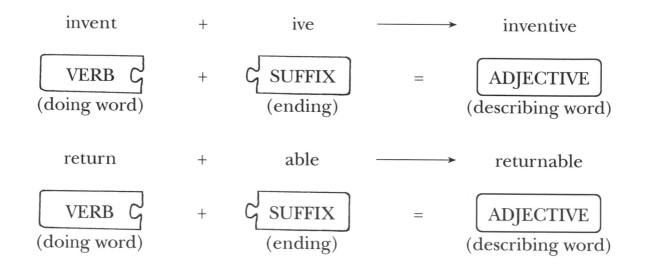

- Use the words in the box to complete the sentences.

A person who disrupts is _____.

A person who creates is _____.

A person who talks a lot is _____.

A person who moves a lot is _____.

A person who pays attention is _____.

Something that can be broken is _____.

Something that can be washed is _____.

Something that can be enjoyed is _____.

Something that can be read is _____.

Something that can be divided is _____.

Something that can be adored is _____.

Something that can be paid is _____.

talkative

attentive

visible

breakable

adorable

disruptive

enjoyable

payable

creative

divisible

changeable

readable

active

washable

SOLVE the RIDDLES

● Try to solve the riddles yourself or find the answers in the mixed-up list below.

1. What is invisible but never out of sight? _____

2. What fruit is mentioned in history? _____

3. What question always has the answer "Yes"? _____

4. What flowers are kissable? _____

5. How can you keep postage stamps from sticking together? _____

   _____

6. What is the difference between a well-dressed man and a tired dog? _____

   _____

7. What nation always wins? _____

8. What word of 3 syllables has 26 letters? _____

9. What asks no questions, but needs many answers? _____

10. What words can be pronounced quicker and shorter by adding syllables to them?

   _____

_____

a. Buy one at a time.

b. The letter **i**.

c. What does Y-E-S spell?

d. Alphabet.

e. The man wears a whole suit, and the dog just pants.

f. Dates.

g. Determi-nation.

h. A doorbell.

i. Tulips.

j. Quick and Short.

Other suffixes can turn nouns to **adjectives**:

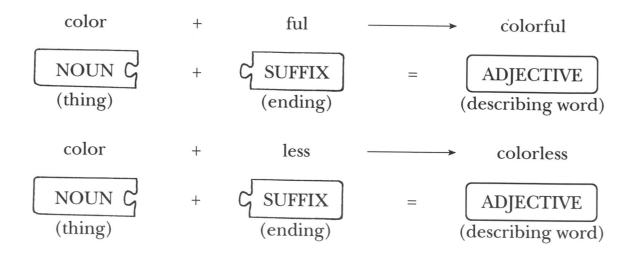

color + ful ⟶ colorful

NOUN + SUFFIX = ADJECTIVE
(thing) (ending) (describing word)

color + less ⟶ colorless

NOUN + SUFFIX = ADJECTIVE
(thing) (ending) (describing word)

● Circle the word in each box that completes the sentence.

A person who is full of fear is _____.	fearless fearful
A person who is full of thanks is _____.	thankful thankless
Something that can hurt you is _____.	harmless harmful
Someone without any power is _____.	powerful powerless
A person with lots of hope is _____.	hopeful hopeless
A painting with lots of color is _____.	colorful colorless
Someone without any help is _____.	helpful helpless
A person who is brave is _____.	fearful fearless
Something that cannot hurt you is _____.	harmless harmful
Someone who breaks the law is _____.	lawful lawless

● Fill in the blanks with words from the top box.

_____
Tomato Sauce

_____ **Club**
Meets Wednesday 4:00
Artists, Writers, Inventors,
Builders, Dancers, Actors

Leave
_____
Bottles Here

From _____
_____
CAUTION
To _____
_____

BABYSITTER _____
Call Rosa Rivera
389-4726

Let our _____
solve your mystery

_____
If Swallowed

_____
American Art

NEW!
TOOTHPASTE
_____
TEETH!

_____
**100%
Cotton**

The suffix **ly** changes **adjectives** into **adverbs**.

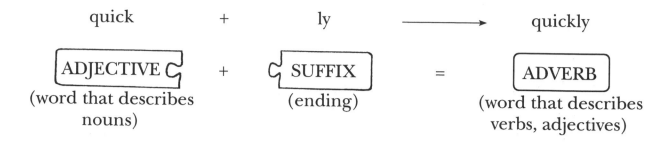

- Draw a line from the word in Column 1 to its opposite in Column 2.

1	2
hotly	weakly
quickly	politely
happily	brightly
rudely	slowly
dimly	smoothly
roughly	coldly
strongly	sadly

- Pick a word from Column 2 to complete each sentence.

1. "Thank you so much," Bendek said _____.

2. The turtle walked _____ to the edge of the rock.

3. The sun shone _____ in the cloudless sky.

4. "I lost my shiny new quarter," said Dawn _____.

5. The wind blew _____ on the shivering children.

6. We all knew our parts, so the performance went _____.

7. Angela tried to shout, but could only answer _____, since she was losing her voice.

Sometimes **two suffixes** can be added to a word:

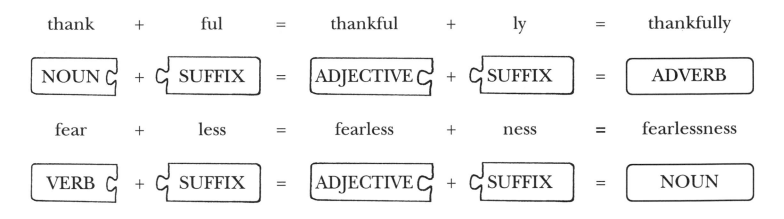

thank + ful = thankful + ly = thankfully

NOUN + SUFFIX = ADJECTIVE + SUFFIX = ADVERB

fear + less = fearless + ness = fearlessness

VERB + SUFFIX = ADJECTIVE + SUFFIX = NOUN

● Take these words apart.

	Root	Suffix	Suffix
The knight <u>fearlessly</u> faced the dragon.	fear	less	ly
Aunt Asha thanked Zayda for her <u>helpfulness</u>.			
When it rained, the farmers cheered <u>thankfully</u>.			
"Stop that <u>foolishness</u>!" said the dog trainer.			
Hinto <u>carefully</u> made the sand painting.			
The carpenter's <u>skillfulness</u> came from years of experience.			
The litterbug <u>carelessly</u> threw paper out the window.			
The babysitter noticed the baby's <u>helplessness</u>.			
We enjoyed the <u>gracefulness</u> of the dancer.			

Words that have the same meaning are called **synonyms**.

Examples: little — small
woman — lady
over — above

● For each word in Column A, find a synonym in Column B. Write the number of the synonym next to the word.

A		**B**
frighten	_____	1. earth
harm	_____	2. scare
grateful	_____	3. peacefulness
make	_____	4. build
loyal	_____	5. great
world	_____	6. piece
powerful	_____	7. damage
blackness	_____	8. correct
wonderful	_____	9. strong
fearless	_____	10. thankful
right	_____	11. gladness
calmness	_____	12. darkness
useless	_____	13. worthless
part	_____	14. faithful
happiness	_____	15. brave

Words that have the opposite meaning are called **antonyms**.	

Examples:　little — big
　　　　　　　woman — man
　　　　　　　over — under

● For each word in Column A, find an antonym in Column B. Write the number of the antonym next to the word in Column A.

A		**B**
day	_____	1. release
damage	_____	2. night
beautiful	_____	3. thanklessness
harmful	_____	4. ugly
helpful	_____	5. fearlessly
happiness	_____	6. loosen
speechless	_____	7. fix
capture	_____	8. harmless
difference	_____	9. talkative
thankfulness	_____	10. sadness
cheap	_____	11. lightness
tighten	_____	12. expensive
neatness	_____	13. helpless
fearfully	_____	14. sameness
heaviness	_____	15. messiness

Suffixes are word parts that can be added to the **end** of a word to change its meaning. Word parts can also be added to the **beginning** of a word. These are called **prefixes**.

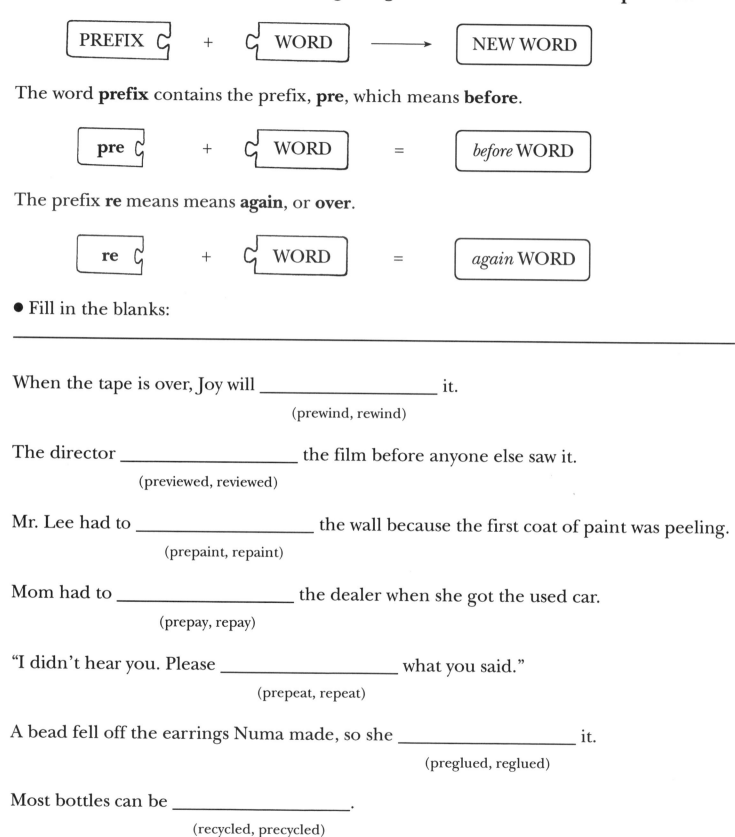

PREFIX + WORD ⟶ NEW WORD

The word **prefix** contains the prefix, **pre**, which means **before**.

pre + WORD = *before* WORD

The prefix **re** means means **again**, or **over**.

re + WORD = *again* WORD

● Fill in the blanks:

When the tape is over, Joy will _____ it.

(prewind, rewind)

The director _____ the film before anyone else saw it.

(previewed, reviewed)

Mr. Lee had to _____ the wall because the first coat of paint was peeling.

(prepaint, repaint)

Mom had to _____ the dealer when she got the used car.

(prepay, repay)

"I didn't hear you. Please _____ what you said."

(prepeat, repeat)

A bead fell off the earrings Numa made, so she _____ it.

(preglued, reglued)

Most bottles can be _____.

(recycled, precycled)

The prefixes **un** and **non** mean "not". The prefix **dis** means "opposite," "wrong," or "not".

● Circle the correct word to complete each sentence:

Something that does not make sense is _____.	sensible nonsense
Something that you cannot break is _____.	breakable nonbreakable
If you can't do something, you are _____ to do it.	unable able
If your shirt is not clean, it is _____.	preclean unclean
If you tell a lie, you are _____.	dishonest honest
If something is faded or stained, it is _____.	discolored recolored
If you don't smoke, you are a _____.	nonsmoker smoker
Before you take off your sneakers you must _____ them.	retie untie
When you get home from a trip, you _____ your suitcase.	unpack repack
If a team always wins, it is _____.	prebeaten unbeaten
If you are sad, you are _____.	unhappy happy
You _____ a door to open it.	relock unlock

The prefixes **uni**, **bi**, and **tri** stand for numbers:

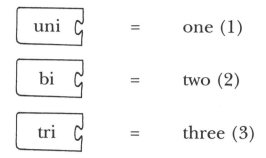

uni = one (1)

bi = two (2)

tri = three (3)

● Circle the correct number:

A tricycle has (1, 2, 3) wheel(s).

A bicycle has (1, 2, 3) wheel(s).

A unicycle has (1, 2, 3) wheel(s).

A unicorn has (1, 2, 3) horn(s).

A triangle has (1, 2, 3) angle(s) or side(s).

A triplet is one of (2, 3, 4) children.

If you hit a triple, you run to (1st, 2nd, 3rd) base.

A biplane has (1, 2, 3) set(s) of wings.

If we are united, we have (1, 2, 3) idea(s).

A biweekly meeting happens every (1, 2, 3) week(s).

To sing in unison is to sing (1, 2, 3) tune(s).

A bicorn animal has (1, 2, 3) horn(s).

A triplane has (1, 2, 3) set(s) of wings.

140

Root words are words or word parts to which prefixes and suffixes can be added. Here are some **root words**:

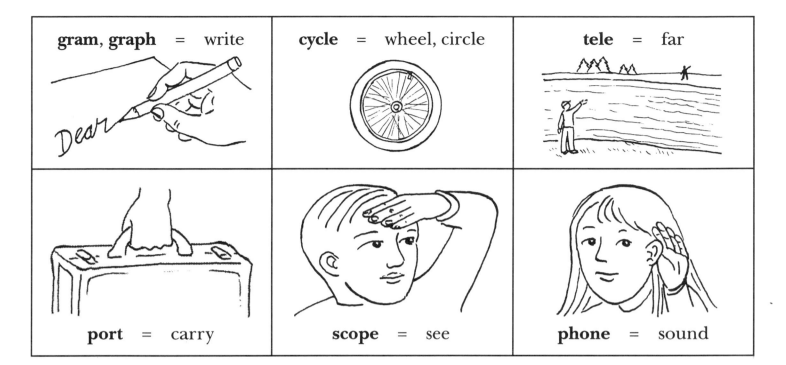

gram, **graph** = write	**cycle** = wheel, circle	**tele** = far
port = carry	**scope** = see	**phone** = sound

● Fill in the blanks:

Tele means _____; **scope** means _____;.
　　　　　　　(far, write)　　　　　　　　　　　　　　(see, sound)

So a **telescope** is something you can _____ _____ with.
　　　　　　　　　　　　　　　　　　(hear, see)　　　　　(close, far)

Bi means _____; **cycle** means _____;.
　　　　　(one, two)　　　　　　　　　　　(wheel, carry)

So a **bicycle** is something with _____ _____.
　　　　　　　　　　　　　　　(two, one)　　　　(wheels, cups)

Tele means _____; **graph** means _____;.
　　　　　　　(far, wheel)　　　　　　　　　　　　(write, carry)

So you can use a **telegraph** to _____ _____.
　　　　　　　　　　　　　　　　(carry, write)　　　　(by, far)

Port means _____; so **portable** means able to be _____.
　　　　　　　(wheel, carry)　　　　　　　　　　　　　　　　(carried, phoned)

● Write to complete each sentence:

Sounds from far away can be heard on a _____.	telescope telegraph telephone
You can see around corners with a _____.	portable periscope recycle
A storm that spins around in a circle is a _____.	bicycle cyclone teleport
You can see faraway stars with a _____.	motorcycle cyclops telescope
You learn about the sounds of letters in _____.	report portable phonics
It has three wheels, and children ride it: a _____.	tricycle unicycle bicycle
You can watch shows from far away on a _____.	tricycle television phonics
A bicycle with a motor is called a _____.	motorcycle unicycle cyclone
A kind of writing is _____.	television calligraphy microscope
It has one wheel and a person can ride it: a _____.	bicycle unicycle tricycle

Prefixes		Base words	
pre	(un)	cycle	tie
re	uni	sense	angle
non	bi	honest	(sure)
dis	tri		

● Solve the definitions below by putting together prefixes and base words from the top boxes.

1. Not certain. u n s u r e

2. Undo a knot or bow. _ _ _ _

3. Make a knot or bow again. _ _ _ _

4. A vehicle with two wheels. _ _ _ _ _

5. Not telling the truth. _ _ _ _ _ _ _

6. A vehicle with three wheels. _ _ _ _ _ _ _

7. Silliness _ _ _ _ _ _ _

● Write the shaded letters in the blanks below. Then circle the underlined word that answers the question.

> Do you read about a
>
> u _ _ _ _ _ _
>
> in a **fiction** or **nonfiction** book?

● Write **true** or **false** after each sentence.

A triangle has two sides. _____

A bicycle has two wheels. _____

If you are unable to do something, you can do it. _____

If you prepay a bill, you pay it late. _____

A unicycle has two wheels. _____

Something unpleasant is not a pleasure. _____

A nonsmoker does not smoke. _____

If you reread a book, you do not read it. _____

If something disappears, you cannot see it. _____

With a telescope, you can see things that are far away. _____

Something portable cannot be carried. _____

A telephone has three wheels. _____

If you replay a game, you play it again. _____

To unlock means to lock up. _____

144

SOLVE the RIDDLES

● Try to solve the riddles yourself or find the answers in the mixed-up list below.

1. When does a chair dislike you? _____

2. Eight women were under an umbrella, but none got wet. Why? _____

   _____

3. What is taken before it is gotten?_____

4. Why is an author an odd creature? _____

5. What driver never gets a ticket? _____

6. What question can never truthfully be answered, "Yes"? _____

7. What is bought by the yard and worn by the foot? _____

8. What runs in and out of town all day and all night? _____

9. What is the difference between a new nickel and an old dime? _____

10. What bird could lift the heaviest weight? _____

_____

a. A screwdriver.

b. A road.

c. When it can't bear you.

d. The crane.

e. Because her tale (tail) grows out of her head.

f. "Are you asleep?"

g. Five cents.

h. Your picture.

i. It wasn't raining.

j. A carpet.

- Help the children finish the school newpaper. Write the best headlines from the lists on the next page.

Our School News

Spring, 1996   Meadow Street School

A

In May, we celebrated the different backgrounds of students and teachers in our school by having a Food Fair. People brought in foods from many cultures. Here are some:

Fou-Fou: African pudding.

Snow Candy: Maple syrup on crushed ice (Native American).

Red Rice and Sea Bream: rice, beans, and fish (Japanese).

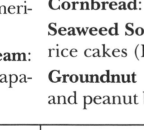

Cornbread: (Native Amer.).

Seaweed Soup: Served with rice cakes (Korean).

Groundnut Stew: Chicken and peanut butter (African).

B

In April we celebrated our planet, Earth. We learned about ways to recycle, so that we don't have so much garbage. We talked about pollution, and how to take care of nature. This holiday was Earth Day.

C

LOST: sweatshirt, gray, size small. Yu-Chen Lin.

FOUND: purple sweater, large. Ask Dan Lopez.

FOUND: silver and black bicycle lock. See Luz.

D

Mr. Ortiz's class measured the school in early June. Meadow Street School is:

230 feet long

180 feet wide

40 feet high

E

The School Nurse tells us to be careful about being in the hot sun this summer.

Put on sun lotion or wear a sun hat, but whatever you do, don't get sunburned!

Have a great summer!

● Circle the best headlines for the newspaper on page 146. Write them in small letters to fit.

A
Food Weighing Fun

Foods of Many Cultures

Kinds of Soups

Gingerbread Feast

Breakfast Feasting

Breads and Butters

B
The Planets

Earth Day

Recycle Cans

Pollution Day

Garbage Goo

Nature Day

C
Sweatshirts for Sale

Found Shirts

Yu-Chen's Shirt

Lost and Found

Small Sweater

Purple Sweater

D
Long Meadows

Teacher of the Year

Foot Wear

Early Birds

Measuring Up

Measuring Cup

E
Be Unhealthy

Burn Lotion

Healthy Nurse

Wear Sandals

Health News

Nurse Leaves

Index